The Journey
"Reflections"

Amber N. Ponder

The Journey
"Reflections"

Amber N. Ponder

Vision Inspired Publications
Atlanta, GA

ISBN: 0985618736
ISBN-13: 978-0-9856187-3-5

Published by Vision Inspired Publications
P.O. Box 44486, Atlanta, GA 30336

www.inspireddivinely.com

PRINTED IN THE UNITED STATES OF AMERICA

DEDICATION

I dedicate this book of reflections to my amazing eighth grade English teacher, Mr. Thaddeus Dawsey. You helped me understand that writing is a style of life.

Thank you for showing me that my writing has a purpose. Thank you for standing by my side even when I didn't believe I could do it.

You have always been there for me to show me the beauty in even one word.

Thank you so much!

ACKNOWLEDGMENTS

Benecia Ponder: for being my support, anchor, leader, person of wisdom and overall my mother. Your words lead me through the day with my head held high.

Grandparents Benny and Bonita Williams: for being there through it all and no matter what always being my pillar of encouragement, support , and LOVE.

Breyuna Williams: for being my aunt, my role model, my helping hand, and a great inspiration in fulfilling my dreams and goals. Thank You!

Ishmael Williams: for always keeping me on my toes.

Great grandparents Myrtle Dansby and Mary Hood: for always encouraging me to do my best and staying the young woman of God that I am.

Marcus Ponder : for caring , loving , supporting, and always having my back through thick and thin.

Ronald Smith, Scarlette Smith, Ryan Smith, Joshua Smith, Franmicka Ford, Richard Ford, and Amari Ford: for supporting , encouraging, helping, and cheering me on in everything I do. You have always been a mountain of love watching over me and I truly appreciate it!

Anthea, Darnell, and William Evans: for loving and helping me throughout my entire life journey so far.

Mama Dan, Dr. Stephanie Smith-Greene (Pookie), and Kare Greene: for caring, loving, supporting, helping, and watching over me making sure I always do my best.

Ashley Phillips: for being a role model, a sister, a best friend, a supporter, a helping hand, and a pillar of love and wisdom. I appreciate our constant talks and your many words or encouragement as I grow up to be a reflection of pure beauty!

Aunt Sandra, Mama Gwen, Mama Evelyn, and Mama Peggy: for always showing me the utmost love and support as I grow to be a wonderful young woman of God.

Grandparents Calvin and Diane Ponder: for loving me to the max and showing me the way of the Lord in everything I do.

Reflections

AMBER PONDER

My Words To You

The words you are about to read are my reflections on the world around me. Some of these reflections are of my own life's story while others are my perspective on the journey of others.

I have taken many creative liberties in writing my reflections and have even made up my own word or two...that's just what poets do.

When you read my words you may think I mean one thing when I am talking about something entirely different.

If challenge you to think deeper and transcend beyond the literal meaning of my words to see the true beauty in human expression.

Enjoy!

.

PENCIL SHARPENER OF AMERICA

In this enormous society all hands reach out like pencils going into pencil sharpeners and this pencil definer, this pencil executioner is America.

The helping hands are being scraped up and down trying to reach its shortest potential.

Metaphorically initializing the blades rotating clockwise are the non-iridescent people cutting my out reaching arm trying to help.

Why won't you take it ?

Do you not want my help?

The help that could lead you to your success.

Take it now or later I won't be here to give it to you.

Take it now or these blades will cut you deep way deep.

Take my hand.

I'm here for you, pushing you forward not back in the days of racism, back in the days of time because American society wastes time.

No entice time of their so called turf.

So take my hand I'll pull you forward so you won't go in reverse.

HOUSE OF HISTORY

Looking through windows of history.

My great inch long arms break down the doors
of my past.

My great inch long legs kicking in the receptor
apitomy filled locked cages.

I currently see myself sitting in the miss-fitted,
ill fitted, unsatisfactory elusive buildup of this
broken down apartment building.

See me, I personally want a big ole mansion
type of house, the kind where my doors can't
get broken down or my cages can't be kicked
into.

My mindset lays curious and filled with fully
secure thoughts and no one can break it down.

Not the "white" house.

Not the small Asian house around the corner.

Not the "what now" Latino house.

Smirk at my shelter not because I know what comes for me.

Smirk at my home because I know not why it comes for me.

All I know and can tell you can never break down my house of HISTORY.

I'LL GIVE YOU ONE

One.

One for every smile you brought to my face.

For every social pattern you raised on my heartbeat.

Calling on you from the womb of earth's surface.

One for every mountain you've helped me climb.

For every ocean you've helped me swim.

To repay you, I thank you.

For the issues you've helped me overcome.

No one is not good enough.

I'll give you two.

Two for all the tear guided posters you put up for my mental   campaign.

Two, for all the angered facial powdered make up you never had to wipe off because my tears did it all for you.

My soul intake breathes these fumes out, disbelieving sights.

No two isn't good enough.

I'll give you three.

Three.

Three for my rushed pen writing the words of my emotions I have been feeling, not for you but for myself.

The days of weariness are over and mental disease never gives away until the heart stops beating.

Until the heartbreaking days of weary and desperation; silent tears are over but I'm not over.

I'll give you ONE

TWO

THREE

Because that's all I have to offer.

DESCRIPTION

Descriptive repository feelings of industrial passion my heart feels for you with all the love and compassion and rage and mutalization, and expression as I walk along the path of your sandy beaches.

The sight of sunrays beaming down on your face.

And all I can hear is your voice, and the thoughts are the only sounds in my imagination.

Lips tasting the fresh squeezed orange mindset you've implanted in my brain.

Description: tall, subtle, graceful, all mine.

Not knowing what I hold because you hold it for me.

Not knowing what I see because you describe it for me.

Lovingly, I worshipingly, pleasingly craft your superficial canvas.

Heart beat = check.

Pulse = check

My heart = check

My description matches yours perfectly.

CARRY ON

Love measured by test results and he realizes affection.

Sometimes comes with strings attached.

In spite of all he can't seem to stop dancing, bopping his head to the beat of a broken home.

Awaking every morning, his flesh feeling like firecrackers.

No wonder he doesn't really allow people to touch anymore.

They tell him he's bright, but it's only because they can't see that he's burning alive.

Keeps all the fury hidden beneath the surface of his clothing hoping no one notices he's a human being underneath the performer.

And those tears can grow a garden, a late bloomer who knows that his poems are pointless.

In a city where every toddler is a tombstone in waiting.

Never really understood gangs but he finds it ironic that blood is blue when its inside of our veins and wonder if there are any Bloods that know this.

And the boy, I mean young man, wonders would you still love him if he never touched the stage, if they would bury him in a microphone stand just so that you can recognize his face when he is on the other side.

Telling the truth.

I can say the truth is—I wish I could have written this in first person.

So I spit these rhymes like bad recipes.

Recognizing the immensity of God's divinity.

Responding with the totality of our own humanity because some fathers are like Jesus himself, you never see them, but you know they exist.

Lions, and tigers, and COWARDS, oh my.

His music wrenching with the most love he could have had from the DNA test scores of not being AB negative, instead he's HIV positive.

In spite of all he can't seem to stop dancing knowing his beat is only one module away.

AMBER PONDER

BITE THE BULLET

Sarcasm spread wide unto distant outbreaks on the indifferent land barrier African island we like to call home.

Being with the luminescent bound replay tryout for the metaphoric NBA (National Black Allegiance).

Loving the all-powerful beam of joy coming in my path from the issued blood filled bath.

Partaking my ancestors' living, hath being what I call this intriguing warrior style look.

We, when we are old—hair the color of tombstones' bones are awakened by the sound of wet windshield wipers trying to wipe away— the wipe away of my distant past times.

Frowns that make the wrinkles in the corner of your eyes look like willow branches all lifting their heads from prayer in unison, and I ask one question.

Five oceans away from my family pictures
downloading on my retina, the cornea awaiting
on my brain to be tagged.

Peeling the night from the sky's skin like the
rind of an orange.

We haven't stopped aching, knowing my best is
coming soon.

Being me , the spoken wordsmith, my world , a
world away.

Battlefields are the closest things to heaven.

Saying just believe in him.

Well I'm sorry but hand grenades are so much
more easy to hold than prayers.

So I don't know if the Lord can hear me, over
the somber solos of all these bombs.

Wings only meaning one thing, not salvation,
but death.

A black hawk becomes the sweet chariot to

carry you home.

A flock of triggers flutter in unison, can you hear the moan, musical moments where bones pop out of sockets literally.

Turning my bones into sickles, my eyes into missiles.

Forget lynching, lynching was so last century.

Forget levitates, a 50 caliber can make a grown man disintegrate.

A bomb is thrown in the middle of the desert can anyone hear it .

Yes, it sounds like a generation of African Americans stand on the front line waiting to be shot first.

Sounds like a mother who can't have an open casket funeral for her son because it looks too much like a fireworks display.

My people tired of dying, tired of being taken advantage of, lying in caskets

FRESH TO DEATH.

Mockingbirds killed by a 21gun salute and so
we fly to keep the dirt off our boots .

No feathers left to flap, wingless warriors with
the phantom limbs that still cradle that M-16
like a lost lover hoping the rhythm would rock
him to sleep.

It's hard enough to walk try learning to
exterminate.

Biting the perching thing awaiting to pull that
trigger onto that "X marks the spot" space on
your chest.

It used to be "biting my master to try to
escape".

Now it's "Biting the Bullet" to come in and
open the affiliated gate.

I AM .... TRAYVON MARTIN

In these poems the first line is always the last
line.

I am Trayvon.

Trayvon who, Martin.

Yeah that's me.

Shot and killed at 17 years old.

The coco brown skin determined my place in
this society.

"Boom, BOOM"

Abolition and agony.

My heart stops beating.

My brain stops processing the vital information
I once used to be the person that I am today.

Who knew that in this country brown skin
means bull's eye.

23

As they pour lead into flesh as if blood could baptize these barbarians and make them MEN.

No handcuffs no arrest on a murderer.

I stand as would be successful, would be honored, would be respected.

See when you die unjustly in this hallucinated country, EVERYTHING is a would be.

WOULD be lawyer.

WOULD be doctor.

WOULD be thought of.

WOULD BE FREE BLACK MAN!

Color seems to be irrelevant but as we see today it's not.

Color is the main nominative of this racist dictionary. Like writing pronouns, on the recent sounds, from the illustrated copy bounded life span, on a young man.

When you get shot everybody bleeds.

When you die everybody is buried in black.

This melanin in my skin is a disease and from what I've seen, you THINK you have the prescription.

Defeating injustice, inside poverty.

For my wounded back pounded by gun shots, why not just fight like a man.

Police reports, evidence, and NO arrest.

However, I'm the one wh's dead for no reason at all.

Like a gazelle hazed on by an elusive predatory lion.

This is for Emmit Till and Sean Bell because like ringing bells, mystery will tell.

Burning out of a cold jail cell.

NOT knowing how to dwell on my past lives.

I don't have to be a WHITE man to realize that.

Images dispersed unleashing my soul into
every soul hurt this "incident".

Your acrimony washes your hands on the
integrated towelette of my heart.

BE an activist, a humanist, a look alike Trayvon
Martin.

In these poems the last line is always the first
line.

I am Trayvon.

Trayvon WHO?

TRAYVON YOU.

"REFLECTION"

Year One

1st step to becoming a full time scholar at work

.

Pencils speak for us, minds think for us,
iridescent like figure models walk for us.

Up and down diamond marked hallways, and
only three more steps and we can truly say we
are scholars.

Because now is our time to make our mark.

Year Two

2nd step of this amazing journey to adult hood,
college prep, knowledge is power present.

The illuminating essence bound life of a
student waiting to exhale, waiting to breathe
out words of life, words of intelligence.

I'm not a rapper I'm a writer writing one more
thing than I did last year .

Only two more steps and we can truly say we
are scholars because now is our time to pick up
our mark.

Year Three

Royal blue decisions come out at us, like bears
come out of the woods.

Like "gangstas" come out of the hood.

Like fish come out of water.

Like starfish come out of the sand.

Like imaginary people come out of my ink filled
hand.

Sit up straight , and stare at the leader.

Because somehow we are the leaders of the
followers, followers of the leaders' leaders,
leaders of the followers of the followers.

Catching glimpses of clever phrases, around
about noises taking place every which way.

Only one more step and we can truly say that

we are scholars because now is our time to set
our mark.

Year FOUR

As I compliment the compliment of set
A to set B.

Staring intriguingly as math hosts let
out the exponents' sigh of always being
just one step behind the coefficient.

Mentally adjusting incapable steps to
this equation.

As my numbers speak for me as if my
number sentences always add up.

Like the trees add up the leaves, as if the
birds add up the bees.

Like the clock adds up the ticking.

Like the room adds up the silence.

Feeling immaculate pressure of words
coming from the mouth of this

inequality.

Feeling the distance of the distance formula fall over my shoulder like the rain falls over the ground.

Like a boy falls for a pretty girl.

Professional realizations of the facts of the proportion except the way we are moving, it just can't add up.

My left arm matches your right leg.

My right arm matches your pinky toe.

I clearly do not understand how this makes sense.

But wait, somehow it does.

My equations are symbols of gratitude towards four amazing years of contradicting shade.

Well now we are in the sunlight and we can testify to this wonderful hunger game.

The way about life so in conclusion .....

Here we are.

All was worth the time and effort
because guess what...

only about 5.....4.....3.....2

WE ARE THE SCHOLARS READY TO
LEAVE OUR MARK

ONE!

A COMMITMENT

One

One team.

One vision.

One promise.

Fulfilling life to the fullest is all I can say.

Two.

Two hands.

Two lips.

Two feet.

Holding on and walking to an unfulfilled
destiny.
Three.

Three poems.

Three love letters.

Three words.

I love you.

I miss you.

Words spoken to a calm and misunderstood heart.

Lovely black days turn into white ones, like the color will change anything?

Only changes made will be the anonymous footprint on your left cheek because you thought it was okay to break the commitment you made to me.

Bones breaking, hearts hurting, agonizing aching filled wonders never to see the broad day light.

Horror stories inside the mindset of your own self.

I'm not going to close our chapter, because if I do then I'll lose my page.

And our commitment will have been broken.

One citation to another , and don't you dare plagiarize my words, because then you'll lose all accreditation towards me, and then I won't trust you anymore.

Defining two words to you.

I'll start now.

A = one.

Commitment = promise .

One promise made in the course of a day took my soul and conquered it.

Love and honor and caution, and effectiveness and strength and courage and faith and time fulfill my deepest needs.

ONE SOLUTION
TWO MINDS
THREE IMPACTS

Yours. Mine. The Universe.

AMBER PONDER

MIME: THE PALE FACE OF THE WHITE SOUL

The pale face hides the true target in which cover up the main issue.

As if masks hide anything.

Painting an imaginary box won't keep out the secrets because indeed the way you put up mixed hand expressions try to create their superficial barrier around the stone cold evidence of imaginable consequence of your emotions in your feelings.

Feelings, feelings of wordless passion exploiting pure thoughts.

Hands moving up and down creating an opening into a whole new era.

Pale faces demonstrate anonymous guilt of over a period of four hundred years.

Round about motions lay "crisscross" facing un belief in chains and whips that lay across on the stereotyped black face making this outstanding fantasy an insignificant reality of the risk at hand never believing mysteries upholding light to a dark shadow.

THE KEY

See, to this exploiting motion three dimensional ligament of past determination, my doubt looks to you from a place beyond my heart.

To the foundation beyond my soul.

To the mix of my pure listings gone into wisdom beyond empowerment.

Your locks on like, looks on love, pointless passion going into the doors of mystery to find why you push up chairs against it to keep the most troublesome secrets out.

So much to the point they are busting throughout the windows, through the vents of your heart.

Individually speaking to a point which cannot be spoken of.

My individual necessity is for you to make me a

better me.

Thoughts distinctively loud to the point where I can't even hear the music playing in the background.

Loving you from a point where the points on my grids are making arrows stretching wide and I cannot.

Keeping me out day after day has nothing to do with your self worth and self-encouragement .

The becoming of all gems and somehow I can make you become to give me the key to make you a better one.

WHEN THE COVERS ARE OFF

When my 100% cotton pink and black striped
blanket is off of me, I feel unprotected.

Dreams free to come at a time that's not
obligated.

Admitted by it all the way saturates.

But there are no angels so I never waited.

I would wake up and no one would be there.

Awakening a dark addict free to escape and you
can tell that your life has been hectic.

Every twist and turn through the night
dreaming of ways to only come back shows
your weak side.

But it's not called weak when you really are
scared, giving in daily so you don't say prayers,
wasting time behind their bed sheets, calling

out her name but she can't even speak.

Resurrected EVERY time, but doesn't God understand she doesn't want to be anymore.

As if words could actually work for her, over all those working worries.

Never having time to go to a real job on a real avenue, not some "Please don't touch me" drive to "Help me please" road .

But through all of this she has to learn how to smile.

Her chilly feeling at night comes not from the distance of her and her blanket.

No it comes from a free person running into her as she tries to run away.

And as the late night wind uncovers the whole mystery to her story.

Smiling for real this time, we now all realize that it was just a bad dream!

POETS

Would you believe me if I said that poets are completely different people.

We write differently.

We speak differently.

See things differently as if all we could transfer mental images onto paper metaphorically.

Poets speak what's on their mind.

Even if some people don't agree because we know our opinions mean the most beyond what the naked eye can see.

Abrasive thought upload unto our pallets like moms cooking on a Sunday afternoon.

We have our own special recipe.

2/3 metaphors.

4 dignified ligament of truth.

And ALL the passion in the world.

You see we believe the earth is in our pen and the paper is the blueprint onto how we are going to take over.

We are branches to trees.

Stems to leaves.

Grounds to seeds.

Man, you all need us.

Everything we write is in perspective , going nowhere without a notebook and a pencil.

So if an idea came up sort of like this one won't forget it.

Poets are artists painting pictures through what vivid images just do not give the "umph" it deserves.

We bring the game to you, missing not one detail entitling emotion to a point in which is unimaginable because you don't know how it is to write as if your dying.

Your pencil non stopping not even for breaths or a cramped hand.

Over flowing previewed snaps, caused by that previewed standing ovation and applause and shaking heads in unison.

YOU SEE POETS, we are not ordinary.

Our poetry combining in heavy symmetry unlocking so much glee and maybe a little history.

YOU SEE POETS, we are different, and my new question is "Do you see it in yourself?" because those words are wisdom causing light to a dark night.

Would you believe me if I said POETS are humans too.

We just all sing a unique tune!

AN OLD FRIEND

It started when we were seven.

Swinging on swing sets, playing on the slides at round about playground.

The movements intrigue us and we thought every moment was eternity.

That was the last play date we had.

You moved to Seattle one hot afternoon in July.

July 14th to be exact.

You being eight million states away, let's just say we lost touch.

But one hot day in July.

7 years later.

You came up to me and asked me was it me and I asked you was it you with the biggest grin on my face.

We caught up as he explained his move back to

the big ATL as he said IMY and ILY and the only words that came out my mouth were Me too!

I didn't know that he would be the opportunity of my opportunity smelling his love stricken breath on consecutive hot days in Jul , and it was like he never left .

Loving every ounce of him as we became one flesh in words, and his mind was my pit of wonder as we explored each other's.

As the caterpillar finds its new ability to fly, we should be thrilled over our spirit empowered ability to live differently and faithfully.

Isn't this what we've all been longing for?

On one very hot day in July.

July 14th to be exact .

THIS AIN'T NO MOVIE

Mommy, when I grow up I want to be a princess.

Like the kind you see on TV.

Shiny tiaras and long puffy dresses.

Limos no SUVs.

Mommy when I grow up I want to be a police girl.

You know the kind you see in movies.

Guns and tasers.

You know "Hey sucker man, that ain't groovy"

But later in life I realized movies aren't real.

There are no fairies or princesses because movies do not exist.

You see fairytales allow small minds to dream and come up with things that just don't make sense.

Breakfast with Shrek.

Lunch with the Incredibles.

Dinner with Superman.

But I feel as if I'm having supper with your kryptonite.

Every year you ask me what I want to be.

And I get weaker.

Waitresses asking me do I want dessert or disaster.

But this AINT no movie.

I have no guns made with goo or superhuman strength to swipe off faces of killer enemies.

Don't ask me what character I like because there won't be a serious answer.

Because I know that this AINT no movie.

I'm all grown up and no one ever told me to do

what I wanted to do.

You can't believe.

You can't dream because dreams can't come true.

But I have to stop and realize, at every cross road, Follow YOUR dream.

It is courageous to let your heart lead the way.

I DON'T PLEDGE

Someone once told me that your poem doesn't
start until you start telling the truth.
So I'm calling this my first poem.
A temporary solution to a permanent problem.
Not knowing one's destiny twisted unto the
days of weary.
I simply don't pledge.
Chains and whips hurt a lot when forced upon
a hurt soul trying to say "I Pledge Allegiance to
the ...."
Wait. What?
Not the African flag of my real warriors.
And you wonder why I can't pledge.
Not because it's a sign of defiance or infidelity.
But because I show true passion to the birth
place of my culture.
Ships on seas took me from my ancestral
history.
Believe me when I say "I don't Pledge."
Please don't get offended or insulted.

But I'm not from here.

From the place impersonating my home as an

apartment.

In this life I never know what's next.

I can't even breathe my next breath.

I demonstrate accusations on mental

physicians and loving in wisdom.

Hibernating on death row.

Executed to execution.

Lying flat on our backs to wait for the electric

chair.

Little boys trading tricycles for triggers.

Among walking like walking corpses saying "

That poem has a purpose."

We the color of ink on the page that signed that

pale piece of paper which handed our kin to

different masters.

Mistaking the middle passage 1,2,3 for the

trinity.

ITS NOT, so I can't see how saying a few

words will change that.

So when we're in class and the teacher asks

why I'm not reciting the Pledge of Allegiance, I

will say, looking onto the glorious view of Eden

taking that apple from the poison leaf ,

"I apologize, but it's just not my belief."

DEAR PAST WORRY

Pain is no game every time I run into you.
Fear the size of an anchor on a ship came from
beneath and struck me like a match.
Trying to burn out the current burn out of my
worry.
And you ask me "How did you know I was
coming for you?"
Said like satan on a Sunday.
Said like night to the day.
It said " I wanted you but somehow there was a
hook, like a deadbolt on your ribs, hunting for
your smile through every audience that I also
made miserable. But like an angel you denied
me"
It said " honey all I wanted to do was stencil the
black rain falling from a disappointment cloud.
I'm trying to forget about you like you forgot
about me but dangit you belong to me!
If only in between the shoulders of insanity, if
only for the width of fall.

57

Those days spent walking downtown with you.

I could wrap my arms around the whole

banquet of autumn , but you didn't stay."

And my worry became a widow of hatred and I

grew

stronger like winds in hurricane season and

now I realize that I'm freshly acquitted so this

will be my last letter to you

Good bye.

Sincerely,

A newly born spirit!

MUSIC

Harmonies like heaven and my soul says that it's been sent to thee.

Because I just can't seem to remember what note goes forth in my musical life timeline.

I see the world changing just one step at a time.

So would it be wrong if maybe I wanted me in your mind because I've always had you in mine.

So just this once I don't want the music to stop playing.

Bass in your baritone and I can't help but say you always were a little off key because the accusations in my alto reach immeasurable heights.

Music so loud I can't hear your voice and it occurs to me that the superstitions in my soprano will always carry a tune in the melody of music.

But for right now communication is all we have
and my heart is in your pocket and all I hear is
my soul in your silence .

THE PURPOSE

The purpose is not passionate when I see you pushing a hole through a brick wall you call my heart.

Honestly hurting the only people you call your best friends, but you didn't think about us when you took a handful of sleeping pills just because you thought it was hard.

The purpose is not passionate when I see you shooting red darts at the stone hedge you call my soul.

But denying the dream of reality I can honestly say that you really hurt my heart.

But you didn't think about us when you lied to our faces and burned our worlds like satan in hell.

Bbecause I want you to get well, but to you that's not an option.

Tears flowing that could fill up a well.

So now my heart is pumping so hard that you can't tell what you've done.

Solemnly speaking from a point unspoken of I can say that our worlds are a few worlds away.

The purpose is not passionate when I see you doing the things that are not becoming, and of course you didn't think about us when you took off running in the opposite direction but you knew you always had our loving.

So in this we will stop at nothing to show you the purpose is not PASSIONATE when all your thoughts become unmentionable like bad movies on digital and I wonder the real purpose of your ways.

So for right now let's move slow in time and for every second we waste let it be a record kept

"Yours and Mine."

ABOUT THE AUTHOR

Amber Nicole Ponder is a creative , energetic, God fearing young lady who has been blessed with the ability to see the best in all those she comes in contact with. Secure in who she is Amber is a confident individual who takes on all challenges with the knowledge that she can do all things through Christ that strengthen her. She shares her love for writing with her Grandmother Bonita Williams author of **Dear Daughters** and **A Watered Garden** and her mother Benecia Ponder author **of Prepare to Receive More.**

Amber's talents expand a broad range of gifts. She is a graceful dancer and a force to be reckoned with on the basketball court.

Made in the USA
Charleston, SC
25 February 2013

The Literature of Cinema

ADVISORY EDITOR: **MARTIN S. DWORKIN**
INSTITUTE OF PHILOSOPHY AND POLITICS OF EDUCATION
TEACHER'S COLLEGE, COLUMBIA UNIVERSITY

THE LITERATURE OF CINEMA presents a comprehensive selection from the multitude of writings about cinema, rediscovering materials on its origins, history, theoretical principles and techniques, aesthetics, economics, and effects on societies and individuals. Included are works of inherent, lasting merit and others of primarily historical significance. These provide essential resources for serious study and critical enjoyment of the "magic shadows" that became one of the decisive cultural forces of modern times.

Screen Monographs II

THE CRISIS OF THE FILM
John Gould Fletcher

THE PHOTODRAMA
William Morgan Hannon

SEE AND HEAR
Will H. Hays

THE AMERICAN INFLUENCE IN FRANCE
Philippe Soupault

ARNO PRESS & THE NEW YORK TIMES
New York • 1970

Reprint Edition 1970 by Arno Press Inc.
Reprinted from copies in The Museum of Modern Art Library
Library of Congress Catalog Card Number: 75-124020
ISBN 0-405-01627-1
ISBN for complete set: 0-405-01600-X
Manufactured in the United States of America

NUMBER TWENTY-FOUR
UNIVERSITY OF WASHINGTON CHAPBOOKS
Edited by Glenn Hughes

THE CRISIS OF THE FILM

The Crisis of
the Film

By

JOHN GOULD FLETCHER

1929
UNIVERSITY OF WASHINGTON BOOK STORE
Seattle

Printed in the United States of America

THE CRISIS OF THE FILM

THE CRISIS OF THE FILM

I

o new form of art has ever been brought into the world under such favorable circumstances as has the film; and no new form of art has so little justified its claim to be ranked as an art at all. That is the extraordinary paradox that lies at the root of all discussion of cinema art. When the brothers Lumière, towards the close of the last century, perfected the motion-picture camera, it was at first looked upon merely as an amusing scientific toy: the amount of picture that could be taken at a sitting was only one hundred yards; and no one thought for a moment that the bioscope (as it was then called) could be used to tell an original story. Yet from the first, the new art was popular. I can remember, somewhere back in 1906 or thereabouts, going twice to an American vaudeville performance in order to see one of the early efforts: a thing called *The Great*

K. & A. Train Robbery, if my memory does not betray me. It began with the robbers riding through the desert, dismounting, and halting the train. They climbed into the engine cab and ordered the engineer to continue the run. Then there followed a supreme thrill; one of the robbers walked along the top of the moving train—this I remember very distinctly. He probably climbed down to the inside, for I have a hazy recollection of seeing a scene in which the passengers were held up. After that—if indeed there was any after—I cannot remember. Yet this thing thrilled me at the time, and probably if I could forget all the films I have seen, it would thrill me still.

In those days no one spoke about art at all in connection with the films. The interest was all in a new means of rendering the exciting side of life. The most exalting—and perhaps fatal—gift of the twentieth century to us all has been a quickened interest in life itself: in the extraordinary things that happen to quite ordinary men and women. The cinema-camera fostered this interest and this curiosity. Like the interest itself, it was a product of naturalism. The question in those days was

whether a good photograph could ever be a work
of art—whether a realistic novel could ever be a
work of art. The film came along and sated some
of the thirst for naturalism. Apart from this, the
interest in the film at the beginning was the interest
in something unfamiliar: the interest in seeing
motion actually take place in what we had always
been taught to believe was a stable medium: the
plastic medium. To watch, on a screen, a figure
walking along the top of a moving railway carriage
without falling off, or the camera breaking down,
was to experience much the same sensation as was
aroused in the spectator by the earliest attempts
at flying. The unfamiliar action and the unfamiliar medium triumphed together.

Now things are different. There is nothing unfamiliar now about the cinema. Rather does it
intrude itself into our lives on every side. It has
conquered the West and is conquering the East.
It has grown from nothing to be the third largest
industry in the world. Its big directors and star
actors are able to command a publicity and a popularity that puts to the blush that possessed by kings
and queens. It has even enrolled in its ranks some
of the more intelligent lovers of art, who being

weary of the mingled banality and freakishness of ninety-nine per cent of the painting emitted today, have persuaded themselves that here is a new medium demanding the intellectual mastery of subject of Michaelangelo, the depth of light and shade of Leonardo, the dramatic force of Tintoretto, the rhythm of Rubens, the humanity of Rembrandt, to master. Yet, despite all this, it has not produced any good statement of its real aesthetic aims, any single picture that is admitted on all hands to be a masterpiece, or any other artistic ideal than the ideal of the box-office. Why is this?

II

As I have said, the film began as a by-product of nineteenth century naturalism. The camera in itself has no artistic value; it is merely a recording instrument. It is as essentially unselective as nature itself; the only difference being that it reduces the full play of natural colour to gradations of black and white. The result is that the best of the so-called art-photographers—men like Craig Annan, Horsley Hinton, Edouard Steichen,

Alfred Stieglitz, Alvin Coburn, were forced, in order to produce good photographs, to become trained observers of the degree of light and shade in any given subject; they arranged their material, waited for the favorable moment, took innumerable negatives of the same subject, picked out the best, and displayed their full craftsmanship in the control they exercised over the printing of their happiest efforts.

The motion-picture camera, as such, is even more unselective than the ordinary camera in trained hands. In order to produce a series of instantaneous pictures which, by being rolled off one after the other, render the effect of continuous movement, it is not primarily necessary that there should be any study of composition, any gradation of light and shade, any definite control or arrangement of material. Indeed, all these things merely complicate the film-problem. The most commonplace news-roll is, as far as film-recording goes, as valuable as *The Nibelungen* or *Caligari*. What makes the difference is the quality of mind at work in the latter, which is unapparent in the former. It is a quality of selection, of unity of purpose, of interplay of episode, of pictorial composition and dramatic climax: a quality, in short, of art.

The film, therefore, in so far as material goes, is rooted in actuality. What gives it artistic possibility is that it can combine actuality of scene and of event to a far higher degree than is possible on the stage. It can relate each episode of a long story to its appropriate background. Thus by destroying the artificial unity of time and place advocated by Aristotle, it can create a real unity of time and place. In each moment of a really good film the figures bear some relation to their surroundings, and the surroundings and the figures vary according to emotional repose or stress. Thus the film solves the problem which agitated Ibsen and most of the other great dramatists of the later nineteenth century: how to combine naturalistic fact with symbolic significance. By throwing overboard the spoken word and substituting mimed gesture for verbal statement; scale, lighting, and position for dramatic accent; the "throw-back" and "close-up" for suspense; tempo and rhythm for climax, the film has progressed by employing precisely the resources that the stage, which aims at being mainly auditory in its appeal, is obliged to neglect. Not only is the film purely visual in its appeal, but it makes its claim as a new art form solely on the basis of full satisfaction, indeed exaggeration of visual appeal.   And as it lacks the color that is so essential a quality of good stage or ballet production, it must seek to overcome this lack by concentration on the utmost possible range of psychological and emotional contrast.

It follows, therefore, that the most impressive films are those in which reality and fantasy are in some way interwoven in the very stuff of the story. *The Nibelungen, Faust, Caligari, Warning Shadows, The Gold Rush, The Kid, Metropolis*— the list could be considerably expanded without containing a single exception. *The Last Laugh,* in which Emil Jannings was so magnificently impressive, might perhaps be counted as one; but its pure naturalism was mitigated first by the drunken revel in the middle, with its trick photographs; second, by the theme itself, which was throughout an ironic commentary on the value of a fine appearance as contrasted with the value of a character; third, by the fantastic "happy ending" which was here, for once, appropriate to the subject.   The other great Jannings film, *Variety,* was no exception to the rule that a film must contain naturalistic as well as fantastically imaginary elements, if it is to remain in the memory. The great merit of Chaplin as film artist has been due to the fact that he stumbled upon and has never forgotten the fact that a film must be both realistic and fantastic—both prose and poetry for the eye. He has followed this idea out with the utmost logic, even to the minutiae of his own familiar make-up and costume.

To recapitulate: the film as a purely objective series of photographs is merely a means for rendering, as closely as possible, the variety and full resource of natural appearance in life as both juxtaposition in space and sequence in time; a means that doubtless many of the great Renaissance artists aspired towards, if they did not actually foreshadow (Leonardo and Tintoretto notably).

In the hands of a man of imagination, the film becomes a means not only for rendering this natural appearance, but for displaying through the employment of appropriate time and space the full emotional and dramatic range of a given series of actions: it shows the outer reality and the inner fantasy, the ideal and the objective fact, as juxta-

posed in a single series of circumstances, and yet in
conflict with each other. It makes use of the resources that the stage is obliged, by its very nature,
to neglect: unity through a series of settings as
compared to unity achieved by one setting;
miming and gesture, rapid change of lighting,
scale and speed, as compared to rapid change of
verbal mood, and development of character on the
basis of a single scale of action; typified humanity
(crowds and spectacles, events of wide range and
import), rather than individualised humanity (the
interplay of fantastically absolute characters within a small field of plot activity such as Shakespeare carried to perfection). Above all, the film
is visual art. The theory, popularly held, that
most films would be nothing without their musical
accompaniments, is absurd. Most films of today
are nothing even with their accompaniments—
nothing that any intelligent person with any pictorial or dramatic sensibility need accept. But I
have seen at least one film that remained highly
impressive when seen with no accompaniment
whatever. In any case a musical accompaniment
merely heightens the optical appeal of good film
technique. It is necessary that the musical rhythm

and the optical rhythm do not clash; that is all.
The words that Shakespeare caused to be spoken
on the stage were intended to be more memorable
as sound and sense than the appearance of the setting in which they were spoken; but how many
people can recall the accompaniment to the carefully planned settings of *The Last Laugh* or
Warning Shadows?

III

What is the reason, then, why so few films of
the last fifteen years have been worth preserving?
Undoubtedly it is due to the operation of two very
diverse causes.   In the first place, the great
majority of films shown are the product not of a
single mind, but of many minds.   There is first
of all, the person 'who writes the plot, or from
whose writings the story is taken.   The film has
always proceeded on the assumption that a good
novel or play would make a good film; whereas
neither plays nor novels possess, except accidentally, the sense of plastic contrast and rhythmic
progression that film technique demands.   The
film is a symphony in pictures primarily; and the

adagio, allegro, furioso, or *cantabile* rhythm at which these pictures can be made to move, must be firmly balanced if the effect aimed at is to be achieved. So the libretto must pass through the hands of the director, and it is the degree of his imagination, together with his liberty of choice, the time he can give to the study of the work as a whole, the conditions under which he has to work, that makes of the whole thing a success or failure. After the director comes the camera-man. Many directors, despite their despotic airs, know nothing about taking pictures; and no success can be achieved unless director and camera-man work in close agreement. After this, come the individual talent of the actors and actresses, the costume-designers, the studio-set builders, and a whole host of underlings. The result is that a spectacular modern film is a thing that takes months to plan, more months to create, and that even when created has frequently to be edited, rearranged, and cut to produce the right effect—for about one hour and a half to two hours is as long as the human eye can be held at a pitch of intense attention. Making a film is therefore a highly expensive, laborious, and protracted process, and it

is this consideration which has brought into force
the second group of circumstances which has so far
militated against any understanding of the possibilities and the limitations of the new art.

These circumstances arose through the men-
talities of the great studio-owning and film-
producing firms which have grown up with the
development of the film itself. These firms treated
the film not as an art, but as an industry. To
produce something that could be understood
quickly, sold quickly, repeated quickly, has been
mainly their aim. They were one and all indis-
posed to make experiments that might cost them
a great deal of money and not bring in box-office
returns. Their aim was to give the public exactly
what it wanted, and if they found out that the
public wanted one type of thing, to go on giving
that thing with as little variation as possible.
Above all, they assumed—especially in America—
that what the public wanted was not strong stories,
but favorite actors and actresses. The film actor
not having to say anything, all that was necessary
was to choose handsomely vacuous faces and dress
them up. Thus the film industry achieved from
the outset a *reductio ad absurdum* of the theatrical

star system which it had inherited from the nineteenth century. Instead of concentrating on the
range of pictorial expression possible, it concen-
trated on the exploitation of the personality of one
particular actor or actress.

Nor was this all. Thanks to the coming of the
war at the very moment when the full possibilities
of motion-picture technique were beginning to be
dimly envisaged, America was given a long start,
and the conventional "success-morality" of the
American mob was immediately pressed into service to justify every lapse from artistic and moral
integrity. An intelligent English critic has declared
that the aim of every American film-producer is
to see to it that the hero "gets away with the girl
and the dough" in the end. Things may be a
little better than when he wrote, but it is still
impossible to satirise big business, openly to flout
conventional morality, to make sin both unrepent-
ant and triumphant. There are such things as film
censors in America—. Moreover, it has been
necessary, in order to keep up profits, not to mention employment for the hosts of people engaged
in American film-studios, to produce films at all
times. The result is that the industry has

progressed with the current, seeking its justification, as I have already pointed out, in satisfying a
popular demand. What will immediately appeal
is all that is asked for, either by American producer or American audience. The result is that the
few good films that America has produced have
been good largely through some accidental com-
bination of circumstances, than through any delib-
erately-achieved aim. Certain things were done
and "took on," and were repeated simply because
they "took on," not because they had any obvious
relation to the ability of making a story emo-
tionally interesting or plastically harmonious on
the screen.

Thus it has happened that mere accident has
ruled the production of films from first to last:
accident and the demands of the box office.
Unconsciously the American film has served as
propaganda for the emotional monotony, the
naïve morality, the sham luxury, the haphazard
etiquette, and the grotesque exaggeration of the
comic, the sentimental, and the acrobatic that are
so common in the United States. It has become
not American art, but American showmanship.
And the Russian film, though in its portrayal of

mood it has sought for a deeper and finer range
of naturalism, has consciously been propaganda
for the Russian revolutionary ethic, and has
thereby destroyed its chance of effectively opposing the American conception. Only one race, by
the sheer force of genius, has so far shown us what
the film might be: these are the Germans, with
whom I also rank the Scandinavians.

IV

The reason for the artistic success of the Germans in the first complete stage of film production,
which is now already passing away, is due to the
operation of a racial genius which students and
historians of art have generally overlooked. The
German people, in so far as they have shown any
aptitude for the visual arts, have always balanced
between two opposing concepts of earthly and
familiar realism and boundless fantasy. The land
of the fairy-tale, of the Erl-King, of the Lorelei,
of Faust and Gretchen, the land of the Nibelungs,
of robber-barons and dragons, has always gravi-
tated between the two poles of peasant senti-
mentality and boundless fantasy. Somehow this

art lacks the aristocratic taste and the classic
restraint that is present in Italy; it is as democratic
in essence as the art of the Flemings and Dutchmen, but it has a quality of myth-haunted
imagination which few of the Flemings and
Dutchmen achieved. This will be seen more
readily if we examine for a moment the work of
the three great German artists, Dürer, Holbein,
and Matthias Grünwald.

In all these artists there is to be found the same
blend of highly particularized objective character-
isation and intensely generalised and symbolical
subjective fantasy. Dürer, for example, could
draw very closely and accurately a hare, a walrus,
and even—on the reports of travellers—a rhin-
oceros, and could turn aside from such conceptions
to the *Melancholia,* the *Knight, Death, and the
Devil,* or the *Great Fortune.* The objection commonly made by most art critics is that the two
things do not lie side by side; that Dürer was at
times capably uninspired draftsman, and at other
times unruly fantast, and that the two things do
not fuse in him. But in what single artist do they
ever fuse? Only in the Gothic cathedral, which
is at once meeting-place for the people and proto-

type of the court of heaven, can the two things come together; and the great Gothic cathedrals are communal art. It is not to be wondered at that Dürer, with the sense of unresolved conflict in him between the ideals of the Italian Renaissance and his own atavistic yearnings towards the fairy-tale lore of his ancestors, now was topical draughtsman and now was romantic seeker for a symbolism the roots of which lay far back in the past or far forward in the future! And Holbein, though he devoted himself more strictly to the purely psychological side of portraiture, no less showed himself a scion of the Teuton genius in his accessories: the hour-glass, the skull, the flower in the vase with its suggestion of sentiment, the shelf of books, the carved ivory ball hanging from the ceiling. All these accessories—which the great Italian portraitists disdain—became in Holbein's hands the media for a heightening of interest in the character he had to present. They were not so much accessories as parts of the being he had to paint. In Grünwald we reach the utmost stage of the German imagination. The great Colmar altarpiece is a world which has nothing to do either with Italian discipline and restraint or

Flemish-Dutch realism. We may consider its total effect melodramatic, its piety morbid, its realism and mysticsm both strained to a point of tension where both become monstrous, but the fact remains that the two strains are completely fused here once and for all in a great work which owes nothing whatsoever to any external influence, which is completely German in essence. After its creation, the German pictorial genius languished, thanks to the influx of foreign styles in the Renaissance, and the Teutonic race sought for an outlet in the cultivation of philosophy and music, where we again meet with the same blend of generalised emotion and particularised statement that confronts us in the works of the artists I have just mentioned. The German genius did not revive again for independent pictorial expression until the advent of the film.

What is chiefly remarkable about the film is, as has already been noted, its ability to create a symphony of pictorial expression. It is built up not only on a series of movements ranging from a rapid tempo of mob-scenes to the slow dragging delay of moments of suspense and anxiety, but also it can show the inside of a character working on the outside of an environment, the human mood as reflected in a gesture and a face as opposed to the natural mood as reflected in light, wind, rain, darkness, vastness of space, or scale and proportion of one single part to the whole. But how little do the American film-backgrounds reflect anything that has to do with the lives of their characters! At the best they merely convey the greatness of scale, the impassive epic moods of the wilderness; and it is for this reason that the best and most genuinely American films have been the cowboy films and films glorifying the pioneer, such as *The Covered Wagon*. The one possible exception is that of Charlie Chaplin; but it cannot be insisted too often that Chaplin is not a purely American artist; that one often feels Hogarth, or Dickens, or Rowlandson in him more strongly than anything specifically American. In fact, the American films may owe a great deal of their success in other lands largely to the fact that they simplified the problem from the beginning. Instead of producing something at once imaginative and subtle, they simply strove to appeal to the lowest common denominator of ordinary sentiment. They reduced movement to the slow

advance of armies, varied by the gallop of horsemen, as in *The Birth of a Nation;* they toned down
every situation so as to produce a happy ending
or a triumph of moral virtue; they pointed everything with inexpressive close-ups, and reduced the
rich play of pathos and absurdity that was possible
in the comic sphere to meaningless chases by
policemen, brainless jokes on prohibition or sex,
displays of the vulgarly incongruous—like the
"custard pie" side of the worst Chaplin films and
of his million and one imitators. Finally, they
lavished enormous time and money on the mere
display of the spectacular—on fine clothes, lavish
banquets, immense parades. The American film
industry has above all lacked originality, courage,
and resource. It has left such things to the
despised Scandinavians, Germans, and Russians.

On the other hand, the specific virtue of the
German film has been its daring. Whether we
take *The Last Laugh, Caligari, Warning
Shadows, The Nibelungen, Faust,* or even *Berlin,
the Symphony of a City,* as an example, the same
quality is always present. The best German film
directors and actors alike have realised that what
the film is capable of achieving is, above all, what

the Germans call *Spannung,* that is to say, tension,
either in the sense of slow waves of movement
piling to a climax, or swift variations on reality
and fantasy, or violent hither and thither leaps
between the inner feelings of the characters, and
the outer conditions of their story. And now the
Germans, despite the fact that their best work has
been produced under the constant threat of either
being banned or, what is perhaps worse, badly
imitated by Hollywood's dictatorship of the
American film, seem about to give us the first
complete analysis of the art-philosophy that
underlies their film production. A book has recently appeared in Germany called *The Coming
Film,** which is the first attempt to cover this
important ground in an intelligent manner. A
translation of this work should be attempted; but
the last people who are likely to pay attention to
its conclusions are the Hollywood magnates themselves. They have made millions out of American
stupidity, and successfully crushed Continental
competition, or forced it into line with their own
ideals; and are now busily engaged with a new
toy, the talking film. This, of course, will merely

Der Kommende Film. **By Guido Bagier. Stuttgart: Deutsche Verlags-
Anstalt, 1928.**

confuse the already badly muddled problem of the
relation of the pictures to their musical accompaniment still further, it will be a fresh advance in
sensationalism, and will only serve to remove the
film one step further from anything that can be
remotely called fine art. A complete boycott of
"talking films" should be the first duty of anyone
who has ever achieved a moment's pleasure from
the contemplation of any film.

V

Although the film is not, essentially, a medium
for words, it by no means follows that we ought
not to talk about the film. As a matter of fact, the
more we do talk about it, the better. Nothing can
be more deplorable than the attitude of that small
minority of intellectuals (more common in Europe
than in America) who simply despise the film as
"vulgar" and absolutely refuse ever to poke their
noses inside a motion-picture theatre. As a matter
of fact, all the great artists of mankind have been
aware of, and have known how to deal with, an
element of natural "vulgarity," Shakespeare no
less than Tolstoy, the mediaeval cathedral-

builders no less than Rabelais. Let us remember
the wise words of Ruskin, "Simple innocent vulgarity is merely an untrained, undeveloped blunt-
ness of body and mind. But in true, inbred vulgarity there is a dreadful callousness, which in
extremity becomes capable of every sort of bestial
habit and crime—without fear, without pleasure,
without honour, and without pity." It is this sort
of vulgarity, expressing itself chiefly in preten-
tiousness, that we must do away with in the film;
otherwise we need only expect such phenomena as
The Ten Commandments and *King of Kings* to
continue.

What is the reason why so many people go to
the pictures who never attend a theatre? Obviously, because, for most of them, the cinema (or,
if you prefer, the movies) provides a reasonably
cheap form of entertainment that is more immediately available. But what is it that they actually
expect to get from the motion-picture theatre?
The answer is easy. It is a story. And the Hollywood magnates, no less than the British, French,
and Italian film-producers, are perfectly well
aware of this. They give them a story, usually a
story with a happy ending. And the result is
appalling.

As a matter of fact, of all the methods of telling
a story, this method of telling a story purely by
means of pictures is the worst. It is even less con-
vincing than the method of telling a story by pure
pantomime as practised by the Russian Ballet. In
the case of the adaptation of known literary
material, it has to be helped out constantly by titles
thrown on the screen: the delight of naïve audiences, and the *bête noire* of the person who really
is interested in motion pictures. It usually only
succeeds in telling a story at all by means of out-
rageous faking of the original author's intention.
The psychological interest, the revelation of character from within that are the chief aspects of the
literary author's ability, have to be put aside in
favor of concentration on the purely spectacular
aspect of the scene treated as scene. The result is
that Thomas Hardy's *Tess of the D'Urbervilles*
or Tolstoy's *Anna Karenina* simply become
travestied when transferred to the screen; whereas a tenth-rate novel like *Ben Hur* or *The Four
Horsemen* often makes quite a reasonably good
picture. The audiences that go to the motion-
picture theatres in the hope of seeing a story told,
are simply wasting their time. They would be,

and are, much better employed if they engage in
what is frequently subsidiary to picture-going
among young people: that is, love-making instead
of looking at the pictures.

If some miraculous power could give these
audiences the idea that what the screen was to give
them was not a story at all, but only pictures—that
is to say, pictorial art—the whole motion-picture
industry would take a great step forward. As a
matter of fact, a good film is really an art-gallery
in miniature. It differs from an art-gallery only
in this: it first limits the range of colors to black-
and-white, but as compensation, gives us what no
art gallery can ever give: one picture linked to
another, one picture growing out of another. It is
therefore to the art-gallery what the fully
developed play is to the vaudeville performance.
Instead of a series of arrested bits of reality isolated by gilt frames from each other, it can give
us the whole of a single reality flowing from a
given beginning to a given end, and held in a
single focus. The theme in itself is unimportant;
the growth and development of it is practically all.

Let me illustrate this by an example. Murnau's
Sunrise was said by many film critics to be "weak

in theme." As a matter of fact, almost all the German films have been said to be "weak in theme" by people whose chief demand was for a story. But the fact remains that *Sunrise* is one of the most beautiful sequences of pictures ever shown on the screen. The theme itself was, admittedly, perfectly commonplace in itself; but the pictorial moods through which it was made to pass in Murnau's imagination, were altogether masterly. If only for the sense of night and day and night coming on again, transforming and altering the lives of the characters that took part in it, this series of pictures deserves a high place of honor in the list of film masterpieces. Yet it was not popular, whereas *Chang*, with an even more commonplace theme, was immensely popular. And the only difference is that everyone looked at *Chang*, not for the sake of its theme, but for the sake of its exotic atmosphere; whereas no one looked at all on *Sunrise* with an eye to grasp what treasures of pictorial richness Murnau had found in this simple tragic idyll of city and country, of night and day.

VI

What is the matter with the films, then, is that
no one has been trained to see them; no one, that
is, except a few directors of genius and a
minority of hungry picture-lovers. Although the
motion-picture has actually come of age, it is still
a child in mind, amusing itself with rattles and
dolls, and squalling on the doorstep of the world
for more expensive and wasteful toys. If it is not
to remain a spoilt child, we have to take its education in hand, and quickly.

If one-tenth, or one-fiftieth of the sums that
the Hollywood magnates spend every year were
to be applied to establishing a film university
somewhere in America, we might begin to enter-
tain hopes for the future. At such a university, the
curriculum should comprise the study of drama,
of pictorial art, and of musical rhythm simultane-
ously. The pupil might start on his four years'
course with the Greek plays, which like the best
films, were written on themes that did not matter
much, but carried those themes through a mar-
vellous emotional range of mood; and from these
go on to the Elizabethans, who practically did the

same thing, in a less strict framework, in their plays. At the same time he should study art in the best ancient and modern examples, and learn something of drawing and composition. Finally, he should acquire a fairly good working knowledge of music. The last year, or year and a half, of his course might be spent to advantage in the film studio itself; the pupil learning not only how to take pictures, but also how to act in them. For the technique of film-acting is tremendously misunderstood, as R. P. Messel points out.* The good film actor must act with his whole body; while the stage actor frequently merely speaks the lines with correct intonation.

Until we get something like this, we are not likely to get any advance in film production or appreciation. What we will get, so long as the film remains a business in the hands of the film-dealers, is merely a repetition of the situation existing at the present day; where there are gaudy picture-palaces arising on every side, in a style reminiscent of the Coliseum and the Turkish-bath, to display sensual boredom and spectacular clap-trap; where dozens of third-rate and fifth-rate

---

*This Film Business. By R. P. Messel. London: Ernest Benn, 1928.

actors become, through publicity, the stars of a moment, and fade away a few years later; where director after director succumbs to the lure of rapid box-office returns, and where the few people who have trained themselves to think intelligently of the motion-picture often wish that the motion-picture camera had never been invented at all.

If you have enjoyed this Chapbook,
you will wish to read:

CHAPBOOK NO. 7

LILLIAN GISH
An Interpretation

By EDWARD WAGENKNECHT

Though serious motion picture criticism in America is almost non-existent, *The Crisis of the Film* is the second contribution the Chapbooks have made towards the elucidation of the most popular and the least understood of all the modern arts. The first, Mr. Wagenknecht's *Lillian Gish* was ostensibly a critical appreciation of the only American cinema actress whose art is taken seriously by the great critics of Europe. Actually, it is much more than that: a stimulating summary of the principles upon which intelligent acting and the intelligent appreciation of acting alike are based.

> *Miss Gish calls it "the most precious tribute I have ever received." The* BOSTON TRANSCRIPT *pointed out that it is the first serious critical study of a motion picture artist that has ever been written. The* NEW YORK WORLD *calls it an "aesthetic and critical Song of Songs." And the Seattle* TOWN CRIER *suggests that it is "written in a style that enchants."*

PRICE 65c

UNIVERSITY OF WASHINGTON BOOK STORE

OTHER PUBLICATIONS

NEW PLAYS *for* MUMMERS
                              By Glenn Hughes

Ten dramatic burlesques in rollicking verse, with block-print illustrations by Richard Bennett. $1.50 net.

UNIVERSITY *of* WASHINGTON PLAYS
                              Edited by Glenn Hughes

First Series, 1921 — Contains four one-act plays by undergraduates. $1.50 net.

Second Series, 1924 — Contains six one-act plays by undergraduates. $2.00 net.

Third Series, 1927—Contains six one-act plays by undergraduates. $2.00 net.

UNIVERSITY *of* WASHINGTON POEMS
                              Edited by Glenn Hughes

First Series, 1924—Contains about a hundred poems by undergraduates. $1.75 net.

Second Series, 1926—Contains about a hundred poems by undergraduates. $1.75 net.

Third Series, 1927 — Undergraduate poems, with sixteen illustrations by Wesley Kilworth. $2.00 net.

All books listed above may be purchased directly from the University of Washington Book Store. Books of plays may also be purchased from Samuel French, 25 West 45th St., New York City.

THE
PHOTODRAMA
ITS PLACE AMONG
: THE FINE ARTS :
BY WILLIAM MORGAN HANNON, B.L., LL.B.
SCENARIO EDITOR OF THE NOLA FILM COMPANY.

PUBLISHER
The Ruskin Press
NEW ORLEANS, U.S.A.

TO THE
WASHINGTON LITERARY SOCIETY
OF THE
UNIVERSITY OF VIRGINIA
WITHIN WHOSE WALLS THE
AUTHOR RECEIVED MANY IN-
SPIRATIONS DURING
THE MOST IMPRESS-
IONABLE YEARS
OF HIS LIFE
. .
.

PREFACE

This little work on the photodrama was prepared primarily for the general reader who has neither the time nor the inclination, perhaps, to study the photodrama in detail, and for the connoisseur of the Fine Arts generally who desires to take a dilettante attitude regarding this art in particular. In short, it is prepared for those who are desirous of getting a bird's-eye view of this most ubiquitous, most popular, and newest of the arts.

Though avowedly technical in tone and treatment, this essay, it is hoped, will be relieved of an academic air by its profusion of concrete examples and "modern instances." Indeed, wherever possible, the concrete is given precedence over the abstract.

It is hoped that this little essay will fall into the hands of lovers of the artistic who sincerely but mistakenly believe that the photodrama should be decried as an art-form, and treated with disdain, as the majority of actors and stage-managers of the "legitimate" drama treated it in its pristine days—but only in its pristine days!

Nola Studios   *—W. M. H.*
August, 1915

CONTENTS

THE photodrama, or "silent" drama, is a species of art that is allied to the art of pantomime on one side, and to the drama proper on the other. It is primarily like the art of pantomime in that its actors are voiceless; it is unlike it, in that it possesses no conventional gestures. The photodrama will be compared to the drama proper quite fully hereafter. Meanwhile, it is well to remember that every moving picture "play" is no more entitled to be dignified by the term photodrama than an incoherent vaudeville sketch is entitled to be placed in the category of the "legitimate" drama.

For the photodrama is an art-form that is worthy of the attention of a serious artist. It is as definite in some respects in its construction as the sonnet. String-

ing together a more or less related group
of scenes without dramatic sequence does
not make a photodrama, though, to be
sure, in its early days the moving-
picture play was just such a vehicle of
expression, as the inordinate ubiquity of
the "chase" picture in those days at-
tested. However, it should be said that
the best producers to-day do conform, at
least in a general way, to the standards
of the formally perfect photoplay.

Mr. William Archer, the great dramatic critic, has said that "there are no
rules for writing plays;" and Mr. Henry
James, the eminent Anglo-American novelist, has said, that "the only rule for a
novel is that it must be interesting." Of
course, these two fiats are to be understood in a qualified sense: it is not to be
inferred from them, that the dramaturgic
and novelistic arts are not governed by
certain principles. At the same time, it
must be inferred that the principles gov-
erning the craftsmanship of the drama

[14]

and the novel are not too definitive. And this is true, as any student of these two art-form knows. Contrariwise, this statement could not be accurately made regarding the photodrama or the short-story; for both of these arts have a definitive, well-understood technique. In passing, it may not be amiss to mention that, like the short-story also, the photodrama has reached its highest development in France and America.

The photodrama can, therefore, be measured, so to speak, with a yard stick. Indeed, in a strictly physical sense, the photodrama is measured in feet, and the length of "footage" bears a direct relationship to the kind of photodrama that can be produced within its compass, just as the size, shape and physical appointments of the "legitimate" stage have always directly determined the kind of drama that could be produced upon it. For instance, the mechanical and lighting equipment of the modern stage permits a degree of realism that was undreamt of in the Greek or Elizabethan drama. And in the photodrama there is permitted a treatment of theme that is extensive and panoramic (rather than intensive and microscopic) in a fashion that no stage of ancient or modern times could hope to equal, still less surpass.

Though the technique and dramaturgy of the photodrama are in their present status nicely balanced, they are dynamic rather than static, and are constantly employing new expedients for their development. Strange as it might at first sight appear, literature proper lends very little aid comparatively to the photodrama. Indeed, the literary content of even the best written photodrama is such a negligible quantity, that one might well question its place among the literary forms proper, as, say, the essay or the oration. But when one remembers that even in the drama proper, the message to the audience is usually more visual than auditory, the fact becomes more patent. And when it is recognized that a good pantomime is the basis of many good dramas, a higher respect is felt for the photodrama as a medium of artistic expression.

The photodrama is at once a mechanical and a fine art. A discussion of it as a mechanical art would not be germane to the present thesis. Besides, the lay mind can readily apprehend, in a general way, its purely mechanical and scientific sides. But giving the photodrama a place among the fine arts would seem to be a more difficult task. Certain it is that it is a more involved one.

Speaking from a standpoint of Aesthetics, the photodrama is a *representative* fine art, like sculpture and painting, rather than a *presentative* one, like architecture or music. An old treatise on aesthetics would probably call it an "imitative" art. Using the word in another sense, however, it is selective rather than merely imitative, as all good art should be. It would seem, therefore, that the photodrama should be given a place among the "humanities." The photodrama is a fine art, as contradistinguished from the merely mechanical arts, in that it possesses an impalpable, elusive, incommunicable element that technique or craftsmanship or mechanics of any kind can never supply, if the creator lacks real inspirational force. For the great artist is he who treats common things with an uncommon imagination, who, in the felicitous phraseology of an eminent novelist, possesses the "admirable gift of individualizing, of etherealizing the commonplace."

To illustrate this principle from an example from a sister art, the novel: There are probably fifty living American novelists who display in their novels greater knowledge of the novelistic art than Dickens. But will their works compare with those of Dickens for all that ? Most assuredly not. And why ? Because the art of Dickens possesses the "inspiration" that raises it above the commonplace, and makes it vital art. The works of the others represent merely craftsmen. Dickens' works represent a great personality. And so it is in the photodrama. A few artistic directors receive an emolument per annum that runs well into five, and even six figures; while others, with just as much experience, flounder around from studio to studio picking up whatever is to be found.

Artistic sincerity demands that the shortcomings and limitations of an art should be set forth as well as its virtues.

Accordingly, it must be confessed that the photodrama does not seem to lend itself readily to the development of the idealistic and subjective in art. Its great field unquestionably is objective realism, though it also handles romantic themes in great fashion, as, for example, the American photodrama that was taken from a popular novel—"Graustark."

Probably no idealistic picturization on the American screen ever created more favorable comment from the public than did the sumptuous production of "Hypocrites." And justly so. For this production was praiseworthy in many particulars. Yet in its purely idealistic concepts it did not "ring true" in the judgment of the present commentator. In a scene, or rather a series of scenes, in which several persons wearing a distinctly "this-worldly" appearance and manner were shown climbing a mountain side as symbolical of their spiritual uplift, their performance seemed incongruous—somehow at variance with the eternal fitness of things. Some will say that this objection is captious—too impressionistic. Granted that it is impressionistic. Impressionism has always been ranked as a valid school art. Indeed, in a deep and true sense, impressionism rather than exactitude is the aim of all art.   If this were not true an ordinary photograph would be greater art than the greatest painting in the world.   The plain truth is that the photographic processes are too graphic and definite to convey delicately symbolical data.   Photography is too exact—it includes the non-essentials as well as the essential—to give merely the essence of things.   In this respect, the celluloid film is not a great art medium.   In short, the photodrama is not quite equal to the demands of those hyper-aesthetic and super-sensitive souls who expect in all art-products a subtle revelation of the essence of things—nay, what might be termed *the elusive essence* of things.

The photodrama is a complex—nay, a truly composite art.   At first blush, it would seem a deliberate exaggeration to say that a director of photodramas is constantly required to exercise a knowledge of the principles of painting, sculpture, architecture, interior decorating, and landscape gardening. Yet a few simple examples will show how this broad culture is necessary.

Primarily, a moving picture is a—picture! That is too obvious to require statement some will say. But is it, as a matter of fact? Isn't it true that even the average, well-educated person does not know the principles of balance, proportion, and grouping in a picture? Then, a knowledge of the art of painting would be useful after all, wouldn't it? Suppose, now, the director is called upon to build an "interior" set representing an art studio. Suppose, further, that a statue of Venus of Milo is a necessary adjunct of such a scene. The property man brings the director a statue with arms intact! The director approves of this statue. Obviously, a slight knowledge of the sculptural masterpieces of the world with their history would prove very useful to this director!

To take an example relating to the art

of architecture: Suppose the director had under production a Greek drama by Sophocles, and was desirous of getting the proper "atmosphere" by getting "exteriors" showing examples of the best Greek architecture. Suppose instead of using the replica of the Parthenon at Athens that stands on the campus of Girard College in Philadelphia, he used the Rotunda of the University of Virginia which is a replica of the Pantheon at Rome, and and excellent example of Roman architecture. Would not every architect who saw the picture on the screen scorn the idea that its producer was an artist? As for interior decorating, in these days when many people of good taste hesitate to furnish their homes according to their own ideas, it is easy enough to see how a director could commit a faux pas here that would verge on the "tragic." Similarly, a director who ignored horticulture and landscape gardening might show a luxuriant, semitropical flower bed as the product of the rigorous climate of New England. Thus, it is easy to see that a good director must be a versatile, resourceful man— a man of broad culture, wide experience, and infinite tact.

The photodrama, may, under one classification, be divided into three parts: first, the writing of the scenario; second, the actual acting of the various characters; and third, the guidance of the production as a whole by the producer, or, to use a more usual term for the same functionary, the director. Broadly speaking, the writing of the scenario involves creative power; the acting, interpretive power; and the directing, creative, interpretive, and for want of better term, executive power. Thus the function of the director is by far the greatest.

The present commentator is disposed to believe that ordinarily the director is half "the show"—the author, the actors, the scenic artists, and so on, the other half. Certain it is that a poor director can make a flavorless, commonplace production with good actors, a good plot, and good "sets." In a few rare cases, however, the actor or author might carry off the honors single-handed, as it were.

To illustrate this from an analogous set of cases chosen from the "legitimate" field of the American theatre: If the play were by Clyde Fitch, the author would probably be the ascendant; if the play were ordinarily good with David Warfield playing the "lead," the actor would probably be the ascendant; and if the play were ordinarily good with an ordinarily good "star" playing the leading role with David Belasco as the producer, the producer would probably be the ascendant.

To take a supposititious example from the "movie" field: Maintaining a "policy of strict neutrality" regarding the delicate question of histrionic capability, it is easy to name the three most popular photodramatic players in America today. They are: Miss Mary Pickford and Messrs. Francis X. Bushman and Charles Chaplin. Suppose a comedy-drama photoplay written by George Ade is imagined in which these three players have equally good parts. Suppose, further, that Mr. D. W. Griffith were to be called upon to direct this galaxy. Who would get the honors, to use a familiar bridge term ? The chances are the verdicts would be somewhat as follows: The business and professional men in the average American audience would divide their votes between Miss Pickford and Chaplin; the feminine "contingent," to use newspaper English, would find "Francis X." irresistible; the writers and authors in the audience would be tempted to think that George Ade should get the lion's share of the praise; and the people who see the wheels go round in the studios (provided they were not actors, of course!) would probably cast their votes for Mr. D. W. Griffith, the director.

In this connection, a word should be said regarding the comedy element in the photodrama. There are about as few good comedies as there are snakes in Ireland according to traditional reports. Examples of High Comedy or Polite Comedy are certainly rare specimens on the screen today. The horseplay, slap-stick element seems to be the only incense that the producers offer to the Comic Spirit. Fame and fortune await the man or set of men who can consistently give the public good photoplay comedies.

The relationship of the photodrama to the Fine Arts generally has been touched upon. A word should be said regarding the characteristic that distinguishes it and the drama from the other arts. This characteristic—its differentia, as logicians would say—is of course Acting.

An extended discussion of Acting would be out of place in the present dissertation. But it would be manifestly illogical to ignore it in its relationship to the photodramatic studios.

Inasmuch as the message conveyed by the photodrama appeals seldom to the mind proper and never to the ear—as do sparkling epigrams and melodious cadences in the drama—one would naturally expect the gesture work in the "silent" drama to be accentuated. But this is hardly the case. For the note— nay, the keynote—of the best screen portrayals is Repression. Hamlet's advice to the players would serve in good stead here; for to "saw the air" within the range and focus of the searching eye of the camera is a most decided histrionic indiscretion. As would be naturally supposed, facial expression is a big factor in photodramatic acting. To give verisimilitude to the scenes, words of the same import as real life or the dramatic stage would employ, are used by the players. And these improvised speeches give an air of naturalness to the "silent" drama in its finished state on the screen that— that speaks louder than words! But silence is not always golden. For instance: the screen appearance of Madame Sarah Bernhardt—the divine, the incomparable Sarah—was at best but a lukewarm success.

But then it must be confessed that the screen has scarcely produced what critics of the "old school" call actors of "tone" and "distinction." However, due allowances must be made for youth; and certain it is that the photodrama is a vigorous child, to say the least.

Here and there in the present dissertation comparisons have already been made between the photodrama and the drama proper. But no formal comparison or analysis has been attempted. A formal analysis of the photodrama and the drama reveals three essential elements of all narrative; namely, the element of character, the element of action, and the element of setting. In character depiction or portrayal the drama is manifestly superior to the photodrama, particularly in what is commonly known as "character study." In action, many critics think that the two arts are about equal, though the drama would seem to have the "edge" on its rival here. But in setting, the photodrama is infinitely superior to the drama. If a ship and an ocean are required in a photodrama, one actually sees a ship and an ocean (or, at any rate, one thinks one sees a ship and an ocean—which amounts to the same thing!). But in the drama one will probably see a "painted ship on a painted ocean," or what is equally disillusioning, a piece of painted canvas waving "frantically" representing the ocean, and a crude piece of carpentry representing the ship.

Therefore, in a free and beautiful

sense, undreamt of in Greek, Elizabethan or Modern stagecraft, it may be said that "all the world's a stage" in the photodrama.

The photodrama, like the drama since the days of Shakespeare, disregards two of the trinity of unities held so sacred by the Greek dramatists; namely, the unity of time and the unity of place. The unity of action is regarded as highly as ever. Even it is violated in part now and then without very disastrous results, as Shakespeare violated it in "The Merchant of Venice." Broad, general literary and artistic principles, like emphasis and coherence, character development, though scarcely character analysis, balance and proportion, and cognate matters, are as applicable to the photodrama as to the drama. And as to-day sees the triumph of Realism, perhaps Ultra-Realism, in fiction and the acted drama, so also is this fetish worshiped by the devotees of the photodrama. It would seem that this wave of Realism emphasizes the objectivity of art at the expense of its subjectivity; and tends generally, to a surfacial view of things. Hence, Farce and Melodrama flourish in the photoplay, while the higher forms of dramaturgy like Comedy and Tragedy are neglected. In short, the moving picture play is moving only in a mechanical and physical sense to a great extent. When it is moving drama in the sense that it moves the mind, the will, the heart, the soul of man—then, and then only, does it enjoy its highest evolution. But it is on its way! Many brilliant minds are lending their talents to its development, and even its tremendous commercial exploitation has not killed its artistry—nay, has helped it. For competition is oftentimes the life of art as it is of trade.

Now for a discussion of the all-important subjects of plot formation, and "stage conventions" as they apply to the photodrama.

Just as in the drama proper, the plot has its Rising action, its Climax and, its Falling action; so also are these elements present, in the photodrama—that is, the formally perfect photodrama. Again, in line with the famous definition of drama, the essential element may be said to be the struggle between wills. No element should enter into the photodrama—however spectacular or interesting intrinsically—that does not help the furtherance of the plot. This rule should be scrupulously followed because the photodramatic action is conveyed through only one of the five senses— vision.

And this visualization, of course, applies even to the most delicate and psychologic action, such as is referred to by Mr. A. B. Walkley, the well known dramatic critic, when he quotes from Dryden: "Every alteration or crossing of design, every new-sprung passion and

turn of it, is a part of the action, and
much the noblest, except we conceive
nothing to be action till the players
come to blows."

Clever words cover a multitude of
sins in the "legitimate" drama. The
"silent" drama, of course, lacks this
agency. It is a commonplace of the
studios that the plot must be "put
across" through the expedients of "business" and "situation," or not at all.
Mr. E. W. Sargent in his treatise on the
photoplay emphasizes this truth. Dialogue is of the *essence* of drama. Its
analogue in the photodrama—the "cap-
tion" or "leader"—is only an *adjunct*.
This distinction is fundamental.

A good photodramatic plot should be
replete with movement, or rather, to
speak more correctly, a series of movements that grow with cumulative intensity as the plot proceeds. In the
words of a recent American song that
had great vogue: "every little movement

should have a meaning all its own."
This is literally true, and not a mere
play upon words. The movement of a
good plot should be forward, always forward, though, to be sure, through the
element of suspense the movement is
not always directly forward, but follows a see-saw course, as the children
would say. In short, its line of action
may be compared to that of an ascending
spiral.

But to have action for action's sake,
so to speak, is not plot. In such a case
the characters would be what has been
happily termed "plot-ridden." This principle can be illustrated by an extreme example by turning the mind to the "chase"
pictures that were shown with such tiresome regularity on the screen in the
pristine days of the photodrama. In a
certain sense, the "chase" pictures were
ALL ACTION; for it cannot be technic-
ally gainsaid that the actors were mar-
ionettes (thus neutralizing the element

of character), and the panoramic scenes that flashed on the screen were accidental and incidental (thus neutralizing the element of setting).

Therefore, it is plain, that plot is something more than activity. To construct a good plot is not an easy task. Even so great a genius as Charles Lamb despaired of ever mastering the plot of the drama. And the plot is relatively more important in the photodrama than in the drama.

A good plot is an "artful dodger"! It is ingenious while seeming to be ingenuous; it at once reveals and eludes "the point;" it puzzles the brain, yet pleases the understanding; it begets longing and satisfies it; it is deadly in its aim and lively in its execution; it is a certainty that wears a glorious air of uncertainty; in short, it is a subtle, insinuating mechanism that plays hide-and-seek with the imaginations of its spectators.

Aristotle in his "Poetics" as it is translated by Professor Lane Cooper gives a definition of Plot in its relation to tragedy that can be aptly applied to the photodrama: "Plot means that synthesis of the particular incidents which gives form or being to the tragedy as a whole." And when a scenario writer learns that a plot is not a hazy, haphazard affair but a structure that possesses an "architecture" of its own, he has overcome one of the pitfalls into which even a seasoned writer falls now and then.

In the photodrama it is well to have the major crisis, or Climax, and Conclusion coincide. A formal conclusion would almost necessarily in all cases prove to be in the words of Hamlet, weary, stale, flat and unprofitable. As in the drama, the effectiveness of the plot is dependent to a very great extent upon how the paramount element of suspense is handled. The element of plot is so accentuated in the photodrama that a complicated plot seems to be the great desideratum. Mr.

H. A. Phillips in his work on the photo-drama dogmatically asserts this. And mere spectacle, however magnificent, will not take the place of plot. Indeed, a spectacle will often so hide a good plot as to almost "kill" it. For instance Cabiria, which is a monumental work from a spectacular standpoint, is in the judgment of the present commentator, artistically defective because it lacks balance and proportion in that its spectacular effects are so great, so attention-arresting, so to say, that the elements of character and action are obscured. Just as it is a fundamental of good architecture that decorational effects should be structural, so also is it a fundamental of the photodramatic art that the element of setting should be the usual environment of the characters; and not become an end in itself to woo and dazzle the audience, and thereby hide a slim plot and poor acting. To let a beautiful setting run away with the story, so to speak, would be as inartistic as for an architect to put the ornate tracery of a Gothic cathedral upon the entablature of a severe and staid structure like a Doric temple.

There are in the photodrama certain counterparts to "stage conventions" and "dramatic license." For example, the photodramatic convention known as "cheating on the camera"—which consists in a player getting a better position before the camera than his relationship to the rest of the players in the scene would normally justify—is an expedient of emphasis that serves pretty much the same function as "throwing the spotlight" on an actor of the "legitimate," the comic opera, or the vaudeville stage. Similarly, a "close-view" or "bust" is an expedient of emphasis that might well be compared to an actor playing "down-stage" behind the footlights. Then there is the much-used, and frequently abused, "cut-back." This device gives coherence to a photodrama in the same way that the dramatist gives this quality to the drama by repitition of essential lines or business in the drama. The "straight" and "cut-in" leaders really have no counterparts on the regular stage, though they serve pretty much the same function as the old-fashioned "asides" and "soliloquies" did in the drama. In this connection, it is pertinent to remark that some writers regard the so-called "leaderless" script as ideal, whereas others regard this form as being unsuitable for the complexity of the present-day photoplay. In the present commentator's judgment, leaderless script is almost impossible of practical achievement in a worth-while photodrama. Like the famous definition of metaphysics, it is a process of hunting for a black cat in a dark cellar that isn't there!

Speaking of the tendency to overdo the photodramas made from well-known fictive and dramatic works, Mr. Louis

Reeves Harrison, the well-known writer and critic of photodramatic themes, says graphically: "While live people care very little about the ashes of what has burnt itself out, the producer has an idea that a new flame can be blown into them by some modern author of ability and proposes to give both credit and compensation to the author of the ashes rather than of the flame. Right here lies one cause of the tiresome artificiality shown in a large majority of five-reel feature plays." To paraphrase Shakespeare slightly, this is such stuff as many *up-to-date* photodramas are made of! But there are other artistic flaws in photodramas to-day. One of the most conspicuous is the desire of producers to exploit the charms of some bright-eyed, wavy-haired, sprite-like damsel at the expense of the consistency of the plot, the other actors, and so on. Then, too, another artistic fault is the fact that the prolixity of many five-reel features is an inherent defect. It often lies in the fact that the five-reel feature tries to tell too much— to tell two stories unwittingly instead of one sometimes. Many a tedious "five-reeler" could be cut down to a compact, unified three-reel production; and the action strengthened by a few carefully placed captions or leaders in the first part of the first reel.

Since photodramatic productions are in our present-day civilization commercial commodities like cotton and wheat, and since they are governed by the same economic law of supply and demand, it might be well to consider the effect of the public taste on the photodrama. To begin with, one cannot say, a priori, what the public wants. Empirical data alone constitute the guide to the public taste, or rather tastes, to speak more correctly. Neither can the public for long be forced to take what it does not want. And the public is wiser than many caterers to it believes. For instance, it is the public rather than the producer apparently who is discovering that a "star" who scintillates in a "feature" is not the only bright light in the photodramatic firmament!

And to consider any art without regard to the nature of its consumers is to manifest a narrowness of artistic judgment. This is particularly true of the arts that make their appeal to the crowd. And certainly the least cloistered of the arts are the drama and the photodrama.

Modern empirical psychology has established the fact that the mind of the crowd is an entity separate and distinct from the individuals composing it, just as the legal definition of a corporation is that it is an entity separate and distinct from its constituent members. Therefore, a pertinent question is this: What is the nature of the crowd that consumes the photodrama ?

Now, it is a perfectly patent fact that

[43]

no art in the world's history has ever made the wide appeal that the photo-drama has. It makes its appeal to every race and in every clime. It does not have to fight for "a place in the sun"! Nay, it throws its light on the screen on practically every spot on the earth's surface where this luminary sheds its rays. It makes its appeal from Broadway to the Bowery. One is tempted to say that it is a part and parcel of the day's routine in snow-ridden Iceland and darkest Africa.

It is plain, therefore, that the photo-drama is not an esoteric art. On the contrary, its ubiquity makes it the most exoteric of the arts. And when it is remembered that the mind of the crowd of even an intellectual group of people is somewhat primitive in its demands, it is easy to see how elementary must be the human passions depicted on the screen so that the message of the photo-drama escapes "going over the heads" of its spectators. These factors must ever tend to lower the intellectual and artistic level of the photodrama.

In this connection, it might be well to mention that the photodrama has brought to the attention of the general public many classic masterpieces that in their original form were only enjoyed by the art-loving and intellectual few in the quiet of their libraries. A notable example of this is Tolstoy's greatest novel — "Anna Karenina." It is reasonable to assume that only a few thousand Americans have read this work, despite the fact that it is to be found in English translations in public libraries throughout the land. Yet it is fairly certain that the screen production of "Anna Karenina" has been witnessed by over a million Americans. As the greatness of this novel lies primarily in its character portrayals—and hence is not a good subject for screen presentation—this comparison makes a rather unflattering commentary on the taste of the general public. And certain it is that the characters in this novel under the guidance of Tolstoy's genius "get under the skin" in a fashion that makes the screen production, excellent though it is, as inferior to the novel as a photograph is to the living, breathing subject that it represents.

A problem of the day lies in this familiar question: Does the public want famous novels and dramas screened? The answer is simple: the public wants good Photodrama. The public doesn't care whether the stories come from hieroglyphics of an Egyptian temple in ruins, or are the latest products of the best-seller purveyors—except that in both of these instances the stories are apt to be among the oldest in the world! If a famous novel or drama will picturize nicely, why put it on the screen by all means. If not, put it behind a screen and keep it there "till the stars grow cold"! To be sure, there is no intrinsic objection to taking photodramatic material from the drama, the novel or any other form of narrative. Even the mighty Shakespeare took many of his plots from old legends. And Goethe in his greatest work—"Faust"— did the same thing.

But Shakespeare and Goethe only used these plots as "inspirational" material. Their own genius tinctured the working out of the stories to such a degree that the finished products resembled the personalities of Shakespeare and Goethe more than they did the original stories. It is one thing to use material as a source of inspiration; and quite another to transmute a pattern of one kind into an analogous pattern of another kind. Oftentimes this would be as poor art as for a painter to paint from a sculptural instead of a living model. In both cases it is weak, attenuated art because it is a copy of a copy. Besides, the sooner the photodrama stands on its own feet as a distinct art, the sooner will it come into its own in every way.

A discussion often arises as to whether the long or short reel should prevail—as though public taste could be judged by a single touchstone ! Why not have both always? Vaudeville and the "legitimate" thrive in the same communities—nay, for the most part, have the same patrons. Heaven forfend that the photodrama should not be infinitely various, as Stevenson said style should be. To say, for instance, that the multiple reel should eventually supplant the single reel would be as foolish as to say that because Michelangelo covered square yards of space with pigment that the painters of miniatures have no right to existence—as if art were a product to be judged by a quantitative rather than a qualitative analysis !

In conclusion, it might be well to state that the American people should be proud of their great contributions to an art that is primarily indigenous and exoteric rather than exotic and esoteric· And when America lessens its dollar-chasing, nerve-assaulting pace, and devotes more time and thought to the art of living, it may become as great in art as it has in science. Meanwhile just as it might well be proud of the performance of Poe and Hawthorne in literature; of McKim and Richardson in architecture; of Sargent and Whistler in painting; of St. Gaudens and Lorado Taft in sculpture; of Nevin and Herbert in music; of Clyde Fitch and David Belasco in the drama; so also in the youngest of the arts, the photodrama, it might well be proud of the productions of—well, the photodrama must outgrow the follies of its youth before one can recognize its true artists, and separate the sheep from the goats!

WEIGHING WILSON
(An Impressionistic Sketch)

PRECISELY because President Wilson is a democrat spelled with a small "d" is he so eminently successful as a Democrat spelled with a capital "D." But for all that, he is not a typical American. Even the most rabid admirers of America and Americans must, upon reflection, concede this point. P. T. Barnum was a typical American. Like Mark Twain and Jane Addams, President Wilson is a super-American.

President Wilson possesses a catholic and cosmic personality at least in the sense that it runs the whole gamut of paradoxes and contradictions. Hence, we find him preaching democracy from the house tops, and practicing autocracy to perfection; making appointments sparingly, and disappointments even less sparingly; allowing Congress to do exactly as it pleases, provided it does what he pleases; taking newspaper men into his confidence, thereby preventing (let us hope!) his being taken into their confidence; and, above all, we find him to be the bane of politicians, because he believes that what is politic for the people should be the politics of the party.

We hear a great deal of talk nowadays about the "secret of success." We rather fancy that in the case of President Wilson the secret of his success is that it is no secret, for, like everything else tangible or intangible connected with him, it is open and aboveboard. He is a great man for the very simple and excellent reason that he never tried to be great, but is content with being merely good. By deeds, rather than by words, he is teaching the American people that Intellect and Practicality may be found in one and the same individual; and is living down his reputation among so-called practical men as a college professor by living up to his position as

President of the United States. He is proving himself a master of the gentle art of ruling by force and pastmaster of the gentler art of forcing by rule; and would probably state very blandly that he is the ruler of his people whose people's rule rule him.

It may not be amiss to indulge in a few generalities about so vast and versatile a personality as is President Wilson's, for we feel certain that a man of iron can stand a little irony, and that he is sufficiently heavy to be made light of. We have never inquired by what master of delicate and subtle and veiled satire President Wilson's messages to Congress have been written; but we know from eye-witnesses and ear-witnesses that he at least, or at least he (as you please), reads them. We take it that President Wilson was an excellent lawyer before he became a college professor. Indeed, he knew enough about law to quit the practice thereof! And with all due deference, we beg to state that we fancy Dr. Wilson is somewhat of a flirt—he does not seem to know whether he loves the Senate or Big Business the better. Perhaps—we say perhaps—he has a suspicion that the twain are "sisters under their skins." And he is the most reasonable of men in all matters. Why, he does not even object to the Democratic Platform, so long as the performance thereon is carried out in accordance with the Wilson Program!

President Wilson's ability to say much with few words; and, contrariwise, say little with many words, out-Talleyrands Talleyrand. He is virile enough to vitalize a great nation, and yet delicate enough to be "devitalized" by a few of its citizens. He is far-seeing enough to recognize that ultimately American independence may be dependent upon Pan-American interdependence. He has learned that the realm of politics is not a land flowing with milk and honey, and that there may be bitterness in even the Sugar Question! But his ideals may still stand; for, he has also learned that a senator may not be in quest of "pork" just because his name happens to be J. "Ham" Lewis! But if he has learned many things in Washington, so also has he taught many there. Among other things, he has taught "official" Washington that there are two kinds of presidents: those who follow precedents blindly, and those who make precedents with their eyes open!

All in all, we believe he has already shown the kind of leadership that would give him a place in history beside the greatest leaders—if mankind were arrived at that stage of development where a contemporary could be judged as fairly as an antediluvian.

In short, President Wilson is temperamentally a quasi-autocratic humanitarian; educationally, a lawyer; vocationally, a sociologist and historian; and avocationally, one of the greatest executives who ever presided over the American people.

ADVICE TO A YOUNG LAWYER
(A Playful Conceit)

VERILY, verily, my son, thou hast just received the certificate that enableth thee to give forth advice freely; namely, without compensation! Yea, and thou mayst even give it with impunity—to thine own self only!

Wherefore, shalt thou, with all good grace and without compensation or consideration, permit me, thy older advisor, to convey unto thee—the advisee herein, who knowest all the law there is and some there isn't, as well as what the law ought to be—these few words of wisdom in fee, receipt whereof is hereby presumed to be acknowledged by thee with due reluctance.

Thou must remember that law, even as all Gaul, is divided into three parts; to-wit: the case, the client, and the fee— and the greeatest of these is the fee! Wherefore, the last shall be treated of first.

But, my son, be not too happy about the fee; for it is as rare a specimen as the missing link. Yea, and it is often the only link that is missing between the young lawyer and the client; for many young lawyers are consulted, but few are fee-d! Indeed, it were better to be fee-d than to dine, and the latter followeth the former even as the night the day. And it is not true that a fee is the first thing that a young lawyer heareth of when he goeth to the Bar, and the last thing that he ever getteth? But, lest thou lose heart, I say unto thee that it were sound doctrine as regards the fee, that lawyers hopeth where even politicians despaireth!

Behold! if a person by some strange and unprecedented event of Fate entereth thy office to seek legal advice, referreth him to a good lawyer! But if he cometh for the purpose of talking about the weather, offereth him a chair, and if thou hast the milk of human kindness in thy soul and the coin of the realm in thy pocket, inviteth him to lunch. I charge thee that thou never letteth thine ignorance of any point of law worry thee; for thine ignorance may cause thee to do what would otherwise be impossible; namely, giveth thy client sound advice. I charge thee further, that, if in the course of human events—or law practice—thou shouldst be caught giving or having given erroneous advice, thou canst always excuse the above and foregoing act of commission by stating that thou were merely "practising"! And this, above all, it is dangerous to advise thy client too freely—he might follow thy advice!

My son, thou knowest full well what music and magic and mystery there is in a "case," and how thy eyes scintillateth and thy nerves titillateth at the mere mention thereof. Wherefore, I charge thee that it were easier to stoppeth Roosevelt from running for the Presi-

dency for the "Nth" term or to make a
Bull Moose goeth through the eye of a
needle than for a young lawyer to handle
a "case" without high spirits.

But thou desireth the advice herein as
little as a suffragette would desire to
vote if the State permitteth her to do so!

Hence, wilt I close my little discourse,
leaving with thee one final word of hope,
which hath been a maxim since the time
whence the memory of man runneth not
to the contrary and is this: that, notwith-
standing, nevertheless, howsoever, et cetera, badly a lawyer may fail at the Bar,
like the poor baseball player, he always
has a chance of being put on the Bench!

SEE AND HEAR

BY
WILL H. HAYS

*President Motion Picture Producers and
Distributors of America, Inc.*

A Brief History of Motion Pictures
and the Development
of Sound

November, 1929

Acknowledgment is made to Doubleday-Doran for permission to reprint portions of a chapter on motion pictures which appeared in A Century of Industrial Progress, issued by The American Institute.

THE GENESIS
OF THE
MOTION PICTURE

CHAPTER I

*O*NE *stands on a high mountain and sees long lines of men, women, and children moving slowly forward. They come from everywhere. They are rosy-cheeked girls from the farms, and their paler-faced sisters from the cities whose feet ache from long hours of standing behind bargain counters. There are plow boys, and sons of millionaires, and boys with the sallow cheeks of the tenements. There are old women with hands reddened and coarsened by work, and with eyes grown listless with long waiting. There are old men who hobble on crooked sticks, and children with the flash of the sun's gold in their hair and the happy laughter of innocence in their voices. There are the schoolboy, and the savant, and the man of no learning at all. There are men and women of every race and of every tongue, moving slowly forward, seeking something, seeking, searching, yearning—asking for a place to dream. All about them is the roar of the cities, the confused, jangling noises of life that is hurried, rushed, propelled forward at a breathless speed. Every minute of every hour of every day they come—millions of them. And over and above them, and in front of them,*

3

attracting them on, offering that which they desire, are
billions of flickering shadows—the motion picture. Who
shall estimate its importance? Who shall attempt to say
what it means to the world?

The motion picture is the epitome of civilization and the
quintessence of what we mean by "America."

Those are bold, maybe challenging, words; but I believe
that the motion picture's own story, its history and its proper
achievements and anticipations are warrant enough.

Civilization may be said to be made up of four vital com-
ponents: industry, science, art and religion. The motion picture will, upon examination, be found significantly to derive
from and partake of the functions of all these.

Let us set it down immediately: the motion picture is a
great social necessity, an integral part of human life in the
whole civilized world. The thoughtful man can have no
patience with those who would casually pigeonhole "the
movies" with the ephemeral and passing whims that flutter
through the current of amusements. We have had the motion picture now these three decades, developing and explor-
ing its destiny through the ordeals of experience and demonstrating increasingly its fundamental values of service.

It is painfully true that not many, certainly not enough,
people know the motion picture institution. A great many
persons know the fame of screen personalities, a great many
have marveled at the swift prosperity of the industry as
evidenced in some spectacular careers, a vast public patronizes
the screen for its products, but exceedingly few indeed, and
some of them decidedly prejudiced, have given thought and
research and study to the motion picture for itself in its
broader aspects. That is natural enough. In parallel, most
of us want to experience and enjoy health, but we are not on
the whole vastly interested in physiology. But if we are to

realize what the motion picture is and endeavor to think about it intelligently, we must give some heed to its inner facts. No superficial judgment of the motion picture has ever proved correct. Excellent reasons can be found for even its most bizarre manifestations, if one can see the screen from a broad angle, broad enough to take in all the facts.

Civilization follows the tools. The motion picture is the newest, and maybe the best, tool or instrument of the art of expression—and expression is the all of art. By art, man lives the fullness of life. Art is his triumph and release from all limitations of time and place and every manner of awkward fact. Art gives him many lives by vicarious living.

No one can fairly draw the lines that bound art, science, industry and religion from each other. Our civilization is a blending of them all. The motion picture is at once their product and servant.

You can turn to the writings of the scholars and the exhibits of the museums and trace there the entire genealogy of the art and industry of the motion picture as a tool. You will find interesting evidence that the roots of the motion picture run back into the unrecorded beginnings of human consciousness.

It is a fascinating progression that has brought us the motion picture as the newest and best way of telling things, the most direct route alike to the emotions and the intelligence. It began with pantomime, with by-paths into the spoken word, and evolved into drawing, pictographs and alphabets and written language, with other by-paths into sculpture and painting, and with paralleling evolutions of dance and song and ritual and pageantry and lastly drama. Expression ramified into apparently divergent arts as tools developed. All this development was merely toward better ways of telling things, more effective drives into the consciousness of the audience. The motion picture stands in direct line of descent and it is as definitely the offspring and descendant of the first primitive effort to re-create events for others by telling in word and gesture, as the motor car is the descendant of the first ox-cart that creaked over the Aryan plain.

There will be little space indeed to tell any such a complex story here, but an examination into the history of the motion picture will amaze one with the array of savants and priests, and preachers and painters and scientists and magicians who have vitally figured in its evolution.

Expression means making the other man feel what you feel, see what you see. That is all that any of the arts are for, whether the expression is in marble or paint or stage drama or printer's ink. Let us put it down that the motion picture is the new, and possibly final, instrument of doing it and doing it more perfectly than it was ever done before.

We have arrived at the motion picture just about as early as it was possible to evolve it as a new tool from the older tools developed ahead of it. It had to wait on mechanics, optics and chemistry. It came, as so many others of the great new necessities of the new life of our era came, on the wave of American invention, and like all other great inventions it has its debts to the centuries of European endeavor that have gone before.

And let me pause a moment to say here that there are special reasons perhaps why America should have given birth and prosperous nurture to the motion picture as a world art. America is in a very literal sense the world-state. All races, all creeds, all the manners of men that exist on the globe, are to be found here—working, sharing and developing side by side in a reasonable degree of understanding and friendship, more friendship among greater diversities of tribes and men than all the previous history of the world discloses. America's people do not speak of themselves primarily as

Germans, Englishmen, Greeks or Frenchman; as Catholics, Hebrews, Protestants, but as Americans. Ours is probably the least uniform of all nations, in the sense that France is French and Russia, Russian. But it is, at the same time, the greatest single unity among all nations, because America represents a harmony of diversified interests, all of which blend as do the pieces in an orchestra into one deep-toned symphony. Is it not possible that this very quality of harmonized diversities enabled America to express itself to the world by the creation and the development of the world's most universal method of expression—the motion picture? The nation required a method of universal expression. The motion picture is that method.

Thomas A. Edison's desire to give eyes to his phonograph is primarily responsible for the motion picture camera as we know it to-day, according to Terry Ramsaye, historian of the motion picture.[1] Edison was at work, toward the close of the last century, on numerous inventions, but most of his interest was centered on the talking machine with which he had startled the entire world a short time before. William Kennedy Laurie Dickson, a young Englishman, who had traveled thousands of miles in order to associate himself with the Wizard of Menlo Park, was working for Edison and mysterious "goings on" were to be noticed in Room Five of the plant at West Orange.

Conscious scientific endeavor, first as a study of the nature of appearances of motion, and later of the synthesis of appearances of motion, began with the studies of Peter Mark Roget, the same whose name appears on the classic and authoritative Roget's "Thesaurus," first aid to word mongers, who was in 1824 secretary of the Royal Society in Great Britain. After him came many experimenters, notably Joseph Antoine Ferdinand Plateau of Ghent,

[1] A Million and One Nights.

and Simon Ritter von Stampfer of Vienna, and later Lieutenant Baron Franz von Uchatius of Vienna and Emil Reynaud of France. While they studied motion, others, notably Louis Jacques Mande Daguerre and Sir John Herschel and others, pursued the chemistry which gave us photography.

Out of labors started by Roget's studies came a machine which finally became the familiar toy called Zoetrope, using hand-drawn pictures. Then, seemingly unrelated, came a method of recording motion photographically, evolved for Leland Stanford's race horse studies in California, by John D. Isaacs and operated by Eadweard Muybridge about 1880. Jean Louis Meissonier, famous French artist, applied the Isaacs-Muybridge pictures to the Uchatius projecting zoetrope and attained a crude limited sort of motion picture dependent on glass plates. It was only a tantalizing beginning.

Edison abandoned all precedents when he set to work in 1887, and early in 1888 we find the first effort toward the modern motion picture being made in the Edison studios recording the antics of Fred Ott, a mechanic, as the first actor, on a cylinder like that of an old Edison phonograph.

Years later, Ott told of that first performance before a motion picture camera. Repeated by Terry Ramsaye, it is:

"I had a white cloth wound around me and then a little belt to tie it in around the waist so as not to make it too baggy. I looked like a balloon. After I was ready, I made a monkey of myself and the camera was turned."

Mr. Ramsaye speaks of the first picture as "The Follies of 1888." "It was a slapstick comedy staged in a solemn laboratory," he adds with a chuckle.

But the Edison cylinder picture machine, built in simulation of the phonograph, was no adequate solution of the problem. Edison decided he wanted to feed the photo-material into the camera, and the subsequent pictures into a

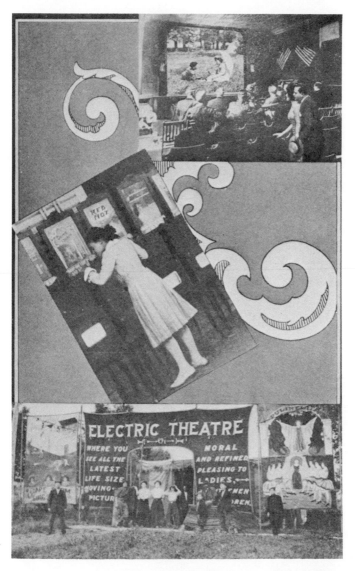

Photos by C. P. Cushing, from Ewing Galloway

Early moving picture days—(Upper) interior of a Nickelodeon; (Center) the peep-show; (lower) The Electric Theatre in the '90's.

viewing machine, on a belt, like cartridges into a machine gun. He was looking for a flexible material to carry the pictures.

Now up in Rochester, George Eastman, who had invented the kodak, had a similar problem for what he called "roller photography." Edison was trying strips of collodion varnish when he heard that Eastman had arrived at a perfected material—for the kodak. Edison sent Dickson to Rochester for a sample.

That first order for film for the motion picture is still in Eastman's files at Rochester. With it went a postal money order for $2.50 in payment for a strip one inch wide and about fifty feet long. That test strip worked.

Imagine the thrill of that occasion. George Eastman's product had met and fitted Thomas Edison's product. *The motion picture had come into being.* And out of their union was to come the new and great motion picture which has since flowered into the world's greatest single source of amusement.

Edison moved on rapidly now in his studio, which, because of its resemblance in color to a police patrol wagon, was known as *The Black Maria*. He was still thinking in terms of eyes for the phonograph. But the moving picture was developing of its own accord. Annie Oakley; Sandow, the strong man; Buffalo Bill; dancers in Hoyt's "Milk White Flag," which was a Broadway success in those days; Ruth St. Denis were being induced to lend their talents to the moving picture, being recorded in single rolls of film fifty feet long for use in peep show machines which were now to appear as a forerunner of the moving picture. The first of the peep shows was opened at 1155 Broadway, New York City, on April 14, 1894.

As the motion picture began to develop into something like regular form and use, the makers of pictures began to consider ways and means of getting popular pictures—a formula on which they are still constantly engaged. They recognized very early that plenty of action was needed and as prize fighting offered action and at the same time had a popular appeal, they turned to the prize fights of the day for filming purposes. James J. Corbett, heavyweight champion of the world, appeared before the camera. He became the first motion picture actor under contract. Later "Gentleman Jim" came back to the moving pictures but many gallons of water had flowed under the bridge between his first and second entrances into motion pictures.

Carmencita, a dancer of current popularity, and Annabelle Moore, who was a reigning favorite in the music halls of New York in the last years of the nineteenth century, also found their way into the new world of make-believe that was to be found in the peep shows of the country. An industry began to show signs of existence.

The public, expressing itself as usual through business, demanded a screen machine, a device which would liberate the motion picture from the peep show. Mr. Edison was not enthusiastic about this, although he had done some research and might readily have solved the problems of projection at once. He had been experimentally projecting since 1889.

An Industry's
Early
Days

Chapter II.

Meanwhile a secret race to the screen was taking place. Probably the first to project, outside the Edison laboratories, was the late Major Woodville Latham, a hero of the Confederacy, from Virginia, who opened a flickering show at about 140 Broadway in May of 1895. Meanwhile in France, Louis and Auguste Lumière of Lyons, and Robert W. Paul of London achieved the screen, and in Washington, Thomas Armat brought forth a projector commercially shown in Atlanta in September, 1895. All of these machines were based on Edison's peep show Kinetoscope and used his films primarily.

Communication was slow then. When the showmen of New York began to demand a screen machine, the Edison agents, Raff & Gammon of New York, investigated Armat's invention, named it the Vitascope, and made a deal at West Orange to have it manufactured and offered as an Edison device—because the market looked to Edison, who was indeed the father of the motion picture.

The first showing was announced for April 20, 1896. The Vitascope was to be the last act on the variety, or vaudeville, program at Koster & Bial's Music Hall at Broadway and Thirty-fourth Street, New York. Delays, however, were to postpone the opening until the evening of April 23rd. The latter date is, therefore, recorded as the real birthday of the motion picture as a form of public entertainment.

It is a fine evening and the house is packed. Silk hats and evening clothes are plentiful. Some of the bloods of the town are here. Thomas Armat is at the projection machine. Thomas Edison sits quietly in a box, acclaimed by the crowd as he was to be acclaimed thirty years later when he modestly visited the opening the great Paramount Theatre, ten blocks north of Koster & Bial's, but now, as on that later occasion, he is silent.

At last the pictures are thrown upon a twenty-foot screen which has been set in a gilded frame. There is the finale of Hoyt's "Milk White Flag," a dash of a prize fight, Annabelle Moore—the dancer—waves rolling in on Manhattan Beach. Marvelous! gasps the audience. Bravo! shouts the gallery boys. As the waves roll in, the first-night audience —at least those in the front rows—jump from their seats and move back through the aisles to avoid being deluged, thus paying involuntary tribute to the reality of motion pictures. Sheepishly they return to their seats to applaud.

Praise! Words of congratulations! Excitement! Newspaper comment! Everybody is speaking of the Vitascope.

The moving picture had arrived. It was now a form of public amusement. Empty stores, holes in the wall, were soon to become alive with moving pictures. A good working machine was put on the market. The public was interested and intrigued. Traveling Vitascope showings aroused the country to eager interest in the new invention. Men, women, and children flocked to see pictures that moved. It was thrilling, exciting—something new under the sun. Farmers left their plows, farm wives their chores, to see Edison's new wonder. An interest was aroused that was to spread to the smallest hamlet, encircle the globe, enlist more people than any other instrument of entertainment the world ever knew.

And with the increased interest came a demand for more

films. From far and wide came the call. People would gladly pay to see moving pictures, but they soon tired of seeing the same pictures over and over again. Novelty in pictures was needed. Thus from the first began the ceaseless struggle for variety of pictures—a struggle which explains why to-day there are 800 feature pictures annually.

The first picture makers had been able to induce some of the Broadway stars and some of the athletic heroes of the country, notably the prize fighters, to appear before the camera. In exchange for their services the stars got splendid advertisement. To-day it is with some justification said that stars demand and receive salaries commensurate with their services to the amusement-loving world.

About this time in the film's history, New York was being treated with what the citizens of that day regarded as a racy comedy called "The Widow Jones," in which Miss May Irwin and John C. Rice exchanged a kiss of almost modern prolongation. The moving picture producers of the day saw the advantages of the kiss on the screen and Miss Irwin and Mr. Rice agreed to reproduce it for the camera. It became an instant success under the rather obvious title of "The May Irwin-John C. Rice Kiss." It was forty feet long and it brought down on the heads of the infant industry several resounding raps. In spite of its popular appeal, a great many people disapproved of osculation to the extent of forty feet and to this day no one has ever definitely determined how many feet long a kiss may be and still remain a proper salutation.

Soon now vaudeville turned eager eyes upon the Vitascope and B. F. Keith houses began to announce it as an added attraction. Newspapers differed in their estimates of its possibilities, but shortly after the Vitascope's first appearance in Boston, *The Boston Herald* took occasion to predict a future. "May not small towns see city shows by the Vitascope?" *The Herald* asked. "May not actresses, who realize how fleeting youth is, preserve themselves in their prime? Indeed to what uses may not the Vitascope be put?" To which *The Boston Traveler* added, "Who knows how the new invention and those that are to follow may revolutionize the amusement world . . . Who knows that each country will not have its stage 'foundries,' so to speak, for each of the various forms of dramatic and musical art? Here finely drilled companies could give performances to be perpetuated by the Vitascope and the phonograph, or by their successors. Duplicates of the records could be sent by flying machines broadcast over the world and London's new play or latest sensational dance could be enjoyed in every quarter of the globe within a few days of the initial presentation."

Did they speak with prophetic tongues?

Busy days followed the introduction of the Vitascope. Bitter days, too. Patent wars were pending and all along the line new activities were to be noticed. The Vitascope had begun to have importance. Men were beginning to see money ahead. It was an open game, as Terry Ramsaye says, and anybody might become important over night. Every man who came in contact with the screen might call it his own. Some heartbreaks, perhaps many injustices, were to be endured before the industry became conscious of itself, of its importance, of its responsibilities and opportunities. But these internal wrangles need not all be told here. They provide a thrilling chapter for the industry, but after all, all industries pass through such periods of unrest and instability. In a great war men die, they are maimed, blinded, diseased. Mothers are bereft of sons, wives of husbands, children of fathers. And yet in the golden sun of victory, these things as lamentable as they are, must be judged in accordance with the great purpose, the ultimate end. In transoceanic flying we see brave young men—and fine young women too—sink to their deaths in the stormy waters. We are grieved; and yet for the future safety of travel, for the greater comfort of those who follow, we persist. These things have to be. It is the story of life itself. And so in the motion picture we find in those last days of the nineteenth century strife and warfare, and not always the most desirable and admirable of methods. But these things we accept now—and with the shaking of a head, pass on, because that past is no more.

We pass on to—the beginning of the motion picture's consciousness of itself as an art. The filming of "The Passion Play" is the first notable move. Now follow such meager attempts at story telling as the filming of "The Life of an American Fireman" by Edwin S. Porter, then an Edison cameraman—a subject, by the way, which was utilized for the screen again in the year 1927, under the more fitting title of "The Fire Brigade." But seven and a half years were to pass from the night the first Vitascope was displayed at Koster & Bial's before a real motion picture with a real plot was to be produced.

"The Great Train Robbery," in which Mr. Porter built upon his technique in "The Life of an American Fireman," is generally regarded as the screen's first effort to tell a story in pictures. It was made by the Edison studios in 1903. Edison was fathering the evolution of the art from the seed of his peep show pictures.

"The Great Train Robbery" was a world-wide sensation. It gave rise to a great development in making pictures with stories. Showmen took to the road with it in black tents and made converts to the motion picture entertainment all over the world. It was followed by "The Great Bank Robbery," by "Raffles—The Amateur Cracksman," and by "Trapped by Bloodhounds, or a Lynching at Cripple Creek."

"The Great Train Robbery" also, by chance, gave the

screen world its first star—Max Aronson, known presently
as G. M. Anderson and later as Broncho Billy. From his
day on, the star has been in the ascendant. The motion
picture public demands its favorites and whatever can be
said for or against the system, the public, as final arbiter,
decides the issue.

On April 2, 1902, the first motion picture theater announced its entrance into the world. The Electric Theatre,
262 South Main Street, Los Angeles, told the citizens of
that city, which later was to become the motion picture capital of the world, that for the price of ten cents it would be
glad to provide an hour's amusement in "a vaudeville of
moving pictures" including "Capture of the Biddle Brothers" and "New York in a Blizzard." Business was so good
on the opening night that matinées started the next day.
In less than twenty-five years, there were to be more than
20,000 motion picture theatres in this country.

"The Electric" was the project of Thomas L. Tally of
Los Angeles, the showman who many and many a year later
was to figure again in screen history as one of the founders
of First National Exhibitor's Circuit, now the world famous First National Pictures, Inc.

There were other tentative beginnings of a screen theater.
So far, the career of the motion picture had been as a com-
ponent of the bills of the variety theaters which were becoming more elegantly "vaudeville." One of the earlier
theaters was opened in 1903 in Newcastle, Pa., by the Warner Brothers, due subsequently to figure conspicuously in
the motion picture story.

Meanwhile the peep show motion picture continued to
flourish in the penny arcades, of the sort that linger still in
the congested regions of the greater cities. These arcades,
trivial as they seemed, were to prove mighty agencies of the
future, drawing to the picture a personnel that was one day

Photos by C. P. Cushing, from Ewing Galloway

Two studio scenes in the early days of motion pictures.

to dominate the industry. Adolph Zukor, Marcus Loew, and William Fox are among those who made such inconspicuous entries into the world of the films. Mr. Zukor, now president of Paramount Famous Lasky Corporation, carries on to-day. Mr. Loew, whose untimely death in the summer of 1927 deprived the industry of one of its most cherished leaders, was the head of Loew's Incorporated, which included Metro-Goldwyn-Mayer, makers of "The Big Parade," "Ben Hur" and other notable pictures. William Fox is president of Fox Film Corporation, producer of many screen masterpieces.

While these men were serving their novitiate as purveyors of entertainment to the public in the movie slot machine peep shows, a mighty transition was impending.

Thanksgiving week in 1905, Harry Davis, then a real estate operator in Pittsburgh, decided to put a movie projector, a piano and some film into a vacant storeroom, along with ninety-nine seats, and see what he could do as a showman, with a five-cent admission. The show was "The Great Train Robbery." The experiment was a world-shaking success. The admissions poured through as fast as the one-reel show could be ground out. The East caught fire with the idea and five-cent motion picture theaters swept the country. Every week saw hundreds of new "nickelodeons" opened. By 1907 there were five thousand of them, all new customers for motion pictures, and making for the pictures a new public. Among the newcomers on this wave was Carl Laemmle, now president of Universal Pictures Corporation and a leader in the industry. He opened the White Front Theater on Milwaukee Avenue in Chicago's West Side and there employed a bright messenger boy by the name of Sam Katz to play the piano. Mr. Katz is now the head of the far-flung Publix Theaters.

The coming of this new market put an extraordinary

strain on the capacities of the producing machine of the motion picture industry of the day. The industry had been torn with internal wars and patent fights in the courts since 1896, the year the screen was born on Broadway.

But now studios had to be built and a stable organization set up. Hit-and-run methods would not serve.

In 1906 both the American Mutoscope and Biograph Company and the Edison interests, major opponents in the patent struggles, set up large studios to supplant their roof-top plants and backyard production methods.

In 1907, D. W. Griffith, a Kentuckian, a bit of an author and a good deal of an actor, ventured about seeking to sell some "suggestions" for motion pictures. They were really scenarios, but the word had not been invented yet, at least not for motion pictures. Presently he was employed by the Biograph Company and walked through that old brownstone door at 11 East Fourteenth Street in New York which was to be the golden gate to fame also for Mack Sennett, who was to evolve a whole separate art of production in motion picture comedy, just as Griffith slightly before him set about laying down the foundation of the real dramatic art of screen narration. That was in 1908.

The motion picture, warring, needed peace. Biograph, in the artistic ascendancy due to Griffith, was about to go to the wall in the commercial and patent war. Then a practical peace for business' sake came in the truce that took form as the Motion Picture Patents Company, formed December 18, 1908, which pooled the patents and licensed every picture maker in America. In his analysis of this complex and trying period, Terry Ramsaye credits this labor largely to George Kleine, then the largest distributor of motion pictures in the world, and to Jeremiah J. Kennedy, a consulting engineer and business expert from downtown New York, who became the chieftain of the organization. Discipline came into the industry for a time and it prospered as never before.

Only a few months later, in 1909, a certain little girl, legally one Gladys Smith, an actress in stock and with one Belasco engagement to her credit, went looking for summer work at the Biograph studio. She told the clerk at the inqury desk that she was "Mary Pickford," her newly-acquired stage name.

Not long ago, a theater in New York put on a special revival of one of Mary Pickford's first pictures—a picture called "The New York Hat." It was crude and quite funny to the sophisticated audience. How they laughed! Back in 1909, it was a startling success. A little, unknown girl in California had written it. Her name was Anita Loos. The story was that of a poor girl who wanted an Easter bonnet, a desire shared by countless of her sisters. A kindly preacher, knowing of her longing and of the hard life she led, sent the hat to her. The gossips in the village—Mae Marsh was one of them—complained. They did not understand and Mary's father said he would force the minister to marry her. That was what the minister wished to do all along as it turned out. The fashionable 1927 audience chuckled, and by their chuckling, they praised the progress that has been made.

It was the kind of picture Mary Pickford was to make famous—the Cinderella story. "Little Mary," as she was known, became a national sensation. To-day Miss Pickford, one of the very few survivors of that pristine period of the screen, continues a vital and important personality of the screen, and to a degree that few outside of the industry know, one of its highly capable executives.

Following Mary Pickford's appearance, a long list of notables came—John Bunny, one of the first of the comedians; Bobby Harron; Mabel Normand; Henry Walthall; James

Kirkwood. At first the actors from the spoken stage did not like the idea of appearing in moving pictures. They considered pictures degrading and vulgar. But the movies were attracting many actors from the stage and they were developing stars of their own. Mae Marsh, Norma Talmadge were being heard from. The names of J. Warren Kerrigan and of Maurice Costello were becoming known. Mack Sennett was getting ready to produce his famous comedies, the first of which appeared in 1912. While Sennett continues to produce comedies, other great names are associated with comedies too, in a list of which are those of Al and Charles H. Christie, who have achieved distinction in this important field.

About this time, Adolph Zukor got the idea of "famous players in famous plays." He secured the American rights to "Queen Elizabeth," in which Sarah Bernhardt played, and from then on the influx of stars was equal to the demand.

Sketching rapidly these eventful years—the names of Lillian and Dorothy Gish begin to appear. Wallace Reid, Clara Kimball Young, Francis X. Bushman, Beverly Bayne, Blanche Sweet are rising stars of the day. The motion picture had now advanced far since that showing at Koster & Bial's. It was time for a new sensation and the new sensation came in 1913 when George Kleine imported "Quo Vadis," which ran for twenty-two weeks on Broadway. The motion picture had arrived definitely as major entertainment. The whole world was interested. And only two years were to elapse until D. W. Griffith's "The Birth of a Nation" opened for a run which was unparalleled until recently. That was March 3, 1915. The picture was shown at the Liberty Theatre at $2.00 top price and, with its appearance, it may be said that the screen had caught up with its older brother, the stage. Before long, Broadway was to be filled with motion picture theaters.

Meanwhile Jesse Lasky, who had already won fame in the world of vaudeville as a producer and executive of first rank, and Cecil B. De Mille, author of many plays and librettos for the stage, had rented a barn in Hollywood, California, and gone to work making motion pictures. The day of making pictures in New York was nearing its sundown. The great West with its salubrious climate, its sunshine, water, mountains, deserts and plains, was beckoning to the movie. To-day we find production centered in California. The explanation is a simple one.

California had everything the motion picture director needed. It was made, apparently, for his uses. And so we have the unusual example of an industry, the production of which is centered in California and the distribution and financing of which are centered in New York, three thousand miles away. This has both advantages and disadvantages. Not only are the natural advantages of each place utilized but the viewpoint of East and West can be better analyzed and turned to use.

"Came the day" soon of the serial in 1913-1914. "What Happened to Mary?" was revealed in countless reels. "The Adventures of Kathlyn" were duly recorded. "Dolly of the Dailies" became a national favorite. We suffered with "The Perils of Pauline" and we puzzled our brows to fathom the "Million Dollar Mystery." Pearl White, Marguerite Snow, Kathlyn Williams, James Cruze were followed every week by an interested public. And so it has been through all the industry's history.

The news reels, too, had come as a definite contribution to the screen. For a long time, as far back as the inauguration of President William McKinley in 1897, in fact, events of historical importance were recorded on motion picture film, but it was not until the inauguration of President Woodrow Wilson that the news reel became a daily enterprise like the

newspaper.   To-day we find half a dozen great news reel
agencies at work with cameramen in every part of the earth
constantly focusing their lenses on every important happen-
ing in every land. They witness the pageantries and the tragedies of nations, show the customs and pursuits of all people, holding up a mirror, as it were, to every phase of human activity with vividness and accuracy.

But, stepping back to catch the thread and flow of development, the motion picture, with its world-wide distribution
and its eighteen or nineteen thousand nickelodeons in
the United States and Canada, had not yet reached its full
status.   It was still a "nickelodeon" business.

Adolph Zukor with his long feature pictures of "famous
players in famous plays" was still fighting an uphill battle
to find a home for the bigger product with the bigger idea.
The old, established interests were holding to the nickelodeon
idea and inertia was against the militant opponent of the
new conception of the films and their function.

But on April 14, 1914, the Strand Theatre opened on
Broadway in New York, a theater on a par with the pre-
tentiousness of speaking stage houses, devoted exclusively to
the motion picture.   The opening picture was a nine-reel
version of "The Spoilers" from Rex Beach's novel, produced
by William Selig, a member of the Patents Company group
who was leaning to the new bigger picture idea.   The Strand
was under the direction of Samuel Lionel Rothafel, the man
whom the world was in years to come to know as "Roxy,"
one of the great showmen of the era.   The Strand was the
manifestation of a new idea which was to triumph.   The
Nickelodeon type theatre lingers only here and there as a
fossil survival like the occasional arcades, and the United
States has approximately 20,250 screen theaters, and the
world total of them is approximately 50,000.

It would be interesting to relate many movements of the

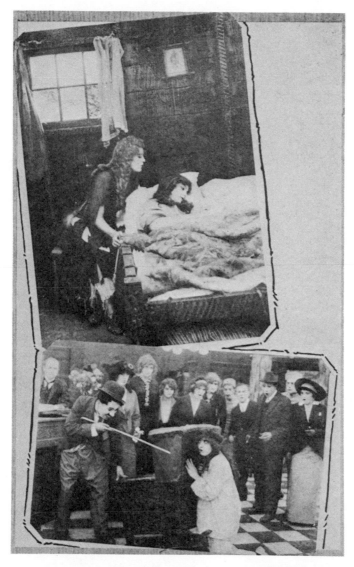

Upper: Mary Pickford in a scene from "Tess of the Storm Country."
Lower: An early Mack Sennett comedy with Charles Chaplin and
Mabel Normand.

busy, crowded years of this period. There is a fascinating
flow of events in the manner in which W. W. Hodkinson
and Herman Wobber brought over to the new order the
best that had been evolved from their experience as pioneers,
especially as that service was applied to the distribution of
the big new feature dramas of Adolph Zukor, Jesse Lasky,
Hobart Bosworth and other producers of the big new feature dramas for Paramount distribution; how J. D. Williams, returning from experience in Australia, brought the
infection of that great commonwealth's enthusiasm for the
art; how Edwin S. Porter, maker of "The Great Train
Robbery," went over to the feature idea with Famous Players, bearing with him the connecting link with the vast technical lore of the original Edison organization. I would like
to tell you the amazing stories of the late William Rock of
Vitagraph and his associates, all famous pioneers, and of Sig-
mund Lubin and of the rise of Stanley Mastbaum, and the
exciting careers of Richard Rowland, Robert H. Cochrane,
Nicholas and Joseph Schenck, Hal Roach and others. They
have labored well and achieved much. And I would like,
too, to tell you of Pathé Exchange's pioneering in the news
reel and of First National Pictures, Inc., being formed by
exhibitors and of Earle Hammons and the Educational Pictures, Inc., but these must be left to more leisurely written
histories, as must be the entrance of Joseph P. Kennedy into
the industry.

I would like to speak of William S. Hart's rise as a great
Western star and hero of boys of all lands, and of Tom Mix,
of like fame; of the first efforts of Douglas Fairbanks, great
artist, idol of boys, who has brought romance and the light
of happiness within the reach of countless listless folk until
they, too, share in the glamor of a new existence; of Hugo
Riesenfeld and the development of music in the motion picture theater; of Jackie Coogan and the child actors; of the

World War and the part the motion picture industry played in it. I would like to talk about Cecil B. De Mille's "The King of Kings"—the potentiality of which cannot be estimated—about De Mille himself, master craftsman, who has dared to go ahead, blazing his own trail with mammoth productions of far-reaching consequence. But I must move on with the sweeping tide that brings the motion picture industry to an appreciation of its importance and of its opportunities.

ORGANIZATION
OF AN
INDUSTRY

CHAPTER III.

Slowly, very slowly, the industry was growing into the consciousness of its own responsibility. The first years of the industry's development were of necessity chaotic. When keen men saw the commercial possibilities in it, they set out in feverish haste on the world-old quest for gold just as the Forty-niners did when word of the discovery came from Sutter's Hill in California. There was competition of the fiercest sort and for that matter there still is. There can be no monopoly of brains, the keystone of picture production. Competition is essential to progress. But the ethics of the competition have evolved. They have mounted constantly. The old careless, helter-skelter days are over. The chieftains of the motion picture now realize their responsibilities as custodians of not only one of the greatest industries in the world but of possibly the most potent instrument in the world for moral influence and education, and certainly one of the most universal mediums of artistic expression. They realize that never before has there existed any means by which the genius of a people could be so swiftly and dramatically presented to all other people and they govern themselves accordingly.

From a business standpoint, the motion picture industry has settled down and is operating along the sound, common sense lines which govern other American industries.

In the latter months of 1921, a growing consciousness of responsibility—recognition of the motion picture as something greater than a casual entertainment for the masses—began to reveal itself. The industry committed itself to an active policy of betterment. Leaders in the industry met and considered what steps to take. The result was an association of producers and distributors known as The Motion Picture Producers and Distributors of America, Inc.

The purposes of that association were chiefly "to foster the common interests of those engaged in the motion picture industry by establishing and maintaining the highest possible moral and artistic standards of motion picture production, by developing the educational as well as the entertainment value and the general usefulness of the motion picture, and by reforming abuses relative to the industry."

These purposes were not to be simply a gentleman's agreement. They were and are legal purposes of a legally organized body. Nine companies were represented at the organization of the Association. To-day twenty-four companies are transcribing those ideals into performances. Those companies are: Bray Productions, Inc., The Caddo Co., Inc., Cecil B. De Mille Pictures Corporation, Christie Film Company, Eastman Kodak Company, Educational Film Exchanges, Inc., Electrical Research Products, Inc., First National Pictures, Inc., Fox Film Corporation, D. W. Griffith, Inc., Inspiration Pictures, Inc., Kinogram Publishing Corporation, Metro-Goldwyn-Mayer Distributing Corporation, Paramount Famous Lasky Corporation, Pathé Exchange, Inc., Principal Pictures Corporation, RCA Photophone, Inc., RKO Distributing Corp., Hal Roach Studios, Inc., Sono-Art Productions, Inc., United Artists Corporation, Universal Pictures Corporation, Vitagraph, Inc., Warner Brothers Pictures, Inc.

Associated with the Motion Picture Producers and Dis-

Upper—A scene from "The Birth of a Nation," D. W. Griffith's production.

Lower.—Thomas A. Edison turned the crank again on Fred Ott, first movie star. The onlooker is Henry Ford.

tributors of America is the Association of Motion Picture
Producers of California, an organization designed to set into
practice the ideals of responsibility and discharge of duty
which actuate every branch of the organized and alert motion picture industry of to-day.

The industry had by now passed beyond the state of an
entertainment force only. The screen was being used in
many directions. It had become an aid to the educator, an
ally of the scientist, the servant of clergymen, the friend of
industries. How were these other agencies experimenting
with the motion picture to get the best results from the
screen? We found isolated instances of schools using pictures to help the teacher. We found a few scientific films
in use. Churches were ready to show religious pictures if
they could get the ones they wanted. Industries were beginning to understand that in addition to showing our clothes,
office equipment, machinery, automobiles, furniture, architecture to all parts of the world, films could perform certain
useful things for industry at home. Motion pictures could
teach employees better methods of operation, more skillful
use of tools, better ways of living, safety methods. To all
these legitimate demands the association turned its attention.

To recite the activities undertaken by the Motion Picture
Producers and Distributors of America would almost require
the time of their accomplishment. Obviously the first needs
were to insure proper entertainment, to insure proper support for the worth-while pictures, and to lend assistance
wherever it was needed in making the motion picture a
greater servant of the world.

The first move was to make sure of the improvement in
the wholesomeness of the entertainment. The motion picture theater is a community meeting house. There gather
the families—fathers, mothers, and children. Motion picture success is based largely upon its ability to please the en-

tire family and the success that has come to the industry, the real affection with which it is regarded by the millions, is genuine proof that the industry is succeeding in that effort.

Many persons have asked, "Why haven't we seen in the movie many of those recent books and plays that deal in themes and situations and topics which in previous years were discussed only in whispers"? The industry was determined that this type of book and play should not become the prevalent type of motion picture and to prevent this, set up *The Formula*, which operates as follows:

When any member company of the Motion Picture Producers and Distributors of America is offered the screen rights to a book or play which that member believes is objectionable, the Association is so notified. If the judgment of the member company is confirmed, the author is advised. He may present to the Association his reasons why the story shall not be rejected; if it is finally decided that the story is unsuitable then the author and all the member companies of the Association are notified.

After a story has been rejected the author may prepare a new story with the unsuitable material removed and with a new title which does not in any way suggest the old title. He may use the proper dramatic incidents and interest making certain only of the elimination of the unsuitable material. Then the author may submit such a new story to the producing companies for picturization, as in the original instance, with the distinct understanding that the film shall not be publicized or advertised in any way that will connect the new story with the old and that it shall not be presented in any way that will mislead theatregoers. If this is not done, then the company members, thus having their attention directed to the subject in question, have the opportunity of avoiding the mistake which the picturization of the novel or play would be.

The method, which is of course thoroughly legal and which has proved efficient, is not censorship in any sense of the word. No censorship could have brought about the results which have been attained. At the same time, the formula does not, by any possible interpretation, limit the production of vital or artistic pictures. Any method which did that would fail absolutely.

To insure support for the better type of pictures, the industry invited great national citizen organizations with millions of members interested in social service, education, religion, civics, to associate themselves with the organized industry in bringing about the results desired. The result was an organization which was unique—a Public Relations Committee. Among the sixty or more organizations represented on the committee were: National Society of the Sons of the American Revolution, National Education Assn., Federal Council of Churches of Christ in America, the International Committee of the Y.M.C.A., Boy Scouts of America, Girl Scouts of America, The American Legion, American Federation of Labor, the National Community Center Asso., Camp Fire Girls, the American Sunday School Union, Chautauqua Institute, Daughters of the American Revolution, National Board of the Y.W.C.A., International Federation of Catholic Alumnae, Russell Sage Foundation, Central Conference of American Rabbis, Associated Advertising Clubs of the World, National Catholic Welfare Conference, American Library Association, et cetera.

The committee had its own officers, a paid secretary, and a smaller executive committee. For nearly three years the Committee was a functioning body. Under its inspiration great interest was aroused throughout the country in supporting the best pictures. Children's performances, known as The Saturday Morning Movies, developed and prospered. In its own office, the Motion Picture Producers and Distributors of America, in co-operation with the Public Relations Group, selected fifty-two complete programs of pictures of special interest to children. They were shown in many theaters throughout the country on Saturday mornings with a standard admission price of ten cents. When the programs became outmoded, they were withdrawn but the movement continued. Now in many cities and towns special Saturday morning performances are given under the auspices of interested public groups who co-operate with the exhibitors, the pictures being selected from the current output of the studios.

In the spring of 1925, the Public Relations Committee, finding the work it had sponsored had become a permanent and actual part of the organized industry, asked that the committee be dissolved and a Department of Public Relations be established within the association. This was done. A small active committee remained and the advice and assistance of the larger group are still gladly received. The policy of the new department became immediately that of "The Open Door." This meant that every individual and every organization wherever located was cordially invited to bring constructive advice and suggestions to the industry. The response has been most gratifying and out of the co-operation have come splendid advancements in many lines.

In 1926, a Department of Industrial and Public Relations was opened in Hollywood in an effort to make sure that the working conditions of motion picture employees was kept the best in the world and to develop still further the material used in the pictures and its treatment. A Studio Committee was organized, with a representative from every studio responsible for what goes into pictures. In advance of production expert advice is asked, from our State Department, from ambassadors from foreign countries, from church groups, education officials, civic leaders, and others whose opinions can be accepted as authentic.

One very concrete example of how the Open Door has helped is to be found in the establishment in Hollywood of an institution that is unique in business—a *free* casting bureau for extra people. The free casting bureau is operated, without cost to the employees, by the producing companies and there are registered eighteen thousand persons who are qualified to work as extras. Some are qualified because they have a wooden leg, others because they possess a fine growth of whiskers, some because they look like Italians or Germans or French, some because they own dress suits and can wear them in a distinguished manner, some because they own horses and can ride them.

These extras work from day to day. Each day's work is a job; 330,397 jobs were given in one year—an average daily placement of 905 at an average wage of $8.59— all without cost to the employee. Their total wages for the year was $2,838,136.30.

Of the average daily placement last year of 905, the number of men per day was 603, of women per day 269, and of children per day 33.

These figures are a blow to the beautiful girls who believe that Hollywood is longing for their art, and for mothers who think their children would add distinction to the movies. An average of only twelve children a day is employed through the casting bureau. These children when at work are under the care of teachers assigned by the Los Angeles Board of Education and paid by the producers. No children may act in the movies unless they are well up in their school work. School hours are maintained in the studio.

In its desire to increase the general usefulness of motion pictures, the industry is cooperating with a church committee in the use of pictures in religious education. After several years of intensive work with great educators, several companies are preparing teaching films for use in classrooms. This method of education will have an enormous effect for good upon the teaching methods of schools and colleges.

Pictures are being shown to immigrants. The films give the newcomers a concrete idea of the country to which they are coming and outline ways and means by which they can become good citizens. Films have been sent to leper colonies in the Canal Zone and in the Philippines and to Eskimos in Alaska. Entertainment is furnished gratis to thousands of "shut-ins" in prisons, hospitals, orphanages and homes.

One of our companies in co-operation with the American College of Surgeons has just completed the first two of a series of pictures for use in clinics and hospitals. Pictures will be made of surgical operations, performed by the masters, in colors, in slow motion or magnified so that the details of the most intricate operations can be studied by surgeons in all parts of the world over and over again until they will be able to duplicate the work of the masters.

In the matter of commercial arbitration, the industry has shown its progressiveness. Disputes arising over contractual relations are necessarily inevitable in an industry of this sort where millions of contractual relations obtain for the showing of hundreds of thousands of pictures. Delays, one thing or another, may bring disagreements. The natural inclination is to rush into court. Pictures can't be tied up by courts. Time is too precious. And so the industry has adopted the arbitration system. In the key cities, there are arbitration boards, each composed of three exhibitors and three distributors.

In the last five years, the arbitration boards have disposed of 73,652 cases involving $17,724,380.82. Only a negligible few cases were litigated after submission to arbitration.

The motion picture, more than any other medium of expression in our modern life, has been hampered and beset by efforts of thoughtless persons to place legal restrictions on its out put. These people have not realized that the integrity of motion pictures must be protected just as the integrity of our churches is protected and that the quality of pictures must be developed just as the quality of our schools is developed.

Motion pictures are not dead things to be regulated like commodities such as freight and food. They are evidences of human thought; and human thought, on which progress depends, cannot be tampered with safely. The tendency to censor, however, remains a mark of our times. The passion on the part of a small minority for regulating and directing other people to their will has become almost a national pastime. The industry's own not unnatural irresponsibilities during its formative years, contributed to the agitation. More recently the very real and personal interest in motion pictures as a means of entertainment and education has made films so much a part of everyday life that some people have appropriated to themselves the right of criticism. Changing conditions, the influx of new ideas and standards, the breaking down of conventions in other relations of life, reaction from the laxity incident to such a world upheaval as this generation knew, submission to governmental orders in stress of war, all added to the prevailing tendency.

So threatening indeed was the political invasion shortly after the termination of the World War, that thoughtful men and women in and out of the industry saw that continued aggression would ultimately mean that there could be no physical distribution of motion pictures in America. The industry, hampered by conflicting laws, would have been forced out of business.

Seven states, by the close of the war, had passed laws providing for censorship of motion pictures—Pennsylvania, Ohio, Florida, New York, Kansas, Maryland and Virginia. Then, after 1921, there began a reaction against censorship based upon the proved ability of the industry to govern itself and the added knowledge by legislators that the people themselves did not want censorship. Three of the seven states—Kansas, Pennsylvania and New York—have recently repealed that part of the law affecting news reels and educational subjects. In thirteen states which considered censorship laws in one year, the measures were overwhelmingly defeated by public opinion.

The only time the people of a state have had the chance to express their opinion, they voted "no." That was in the State of Massachusetts where the censorship of motion pictures was put directly to the people in 1922. The citizens of that state defeated the proposed censorship 553,173 to 208,252—a majority of 344,921 against censorship.

Motion pictures remain the most typical of American productions. Standing well among the first ten industries in this country, the motion picture industry stands first probably in the percentage of the world's supply of a single commodity. These figures issued not long ago by the Department of Commerce at Washington are surprising:

Per Cent.

Of the world's land, United States possess......	6
Of the world's population, our people make up..	7
Of the world's wheat, we grow..............	27
Of the world's coal we dig..................	40
Of the world's telephones, we use.............	63
Of the world's corn, we grow................	75
Of the world's automobiles, we make more than..	80
OF THE WORLD'S MOTION PICTURES, WE PRODUCE MORE THAN	85

Two hundred and fifty-five thousand persons are permanently employed in the industry in this country and more than $125,000,000 is spent annually in production. Last year, 823 feature pictures and several times that number of short subjects, news reels and travelogues were produced. It is estimated that approximately one hundred million Americans go to the movies weekly. Our pictures are shown in seventy countries with titles translated into thirty-seven tongues. Last year, we exported 235,585,000 feet of film and every day approximately twenty-five thousand miles of motion pictures are handled, examined, stored, and shipped by employees in the exchanges of members of the Motion Pictures Producers and Distributors of America.

The future of the industry one hesitates to predict. So great has been the advancement in the narrow scope of thirty-three years that to attempt to estimate the future appears futile. One can see only expansion, development, progress. The motion picture will not only retain its present popularity but will of course add immeasurably to it. It will add also to the list of beneficial services which it already is performing. Producers are taking the best men available into the studios and they are teaching them methods of production which cannot help but result in a steady flow of finer and finer pictures. Universities and colleges throughout the country are teaching motion picture technology and appreciation. All of literature, all of modern writing, provides a wealth of story material. New mechanical developments are coming every day. Theatres are marvels of comfort and beauty. And the producers and custodians of the motion picture in every branch of the industry are aware of the responsibility upon their shoulders.

Thoughtful people are agreeing with our persistent contention that the motion picture is one of the greatest forces yet given to man to bring a happier understanding not only

between men but also between nations. And herein lies
what I confidently believe is one of the greatest future possibilities of the motion picture. The motion picture knows
no barriers of distance nor of speech. It is the one universal
language. All men, wherever they may live, can find on
the screen a story they can understand. If we can only have
understanding, we shall not only be peaceful and kindly
among ourselves, but we shall remain at peace with all nations. When we understand, we do not hate and when we
do not hate, we do not make war.

To promote this international understanding by sympa-
thetically telling the story of the nationals of every country
to the nationals of all others is the determined purpose of our
Association.

The great need of the future, of course, is manpower.
The motion picture business is built largely upon personnel.
Take away the directors, actors, writers and nothing is left
but a highly organized production, distribution and exhibition machine with nothing to keep it running.

The greatest difficulty in progress has been in those phases
of art in which it has been necessary to develop the talent
completely. And there has been the most significant development. It is as if in thirty years from the time man first
began to construct buildings, the Woolworth Building was
erected; as if thirty years after the invention of the violin
we had produced Kreisler, Kubelik and Mischa Elman.

In the late months have come forward so many fine directors, skilled writers and talented actors that the motion picture is producing at least once a week a story that compares
favorably with the best in art, in the drama and in literature.

It is merely a question of finding men and women who
have the talent necessary to make always the very best. Motion picture producers are trying to employ only the directors
and writers who have that ability. They are doing their

Upper—Interior of the Roxy—a Fox theatre.
Center—Paramount Theatre.
Lower—The Capitol, home of Metro-Goldwyn-Mayer pictures.
    All three modern theatres in New York.

utmost to develop them. Directing and scenario writing are two great professions that are a part of this and no other enterprise. Applications by the thousands come from persons who want to write scenarios or direct pictures. In most cases they are persons who are not qualified to pass even the first test. The result will be a mass movement upward. Men and women will come to the industry already prepared in the fundamentals of the business they are to follow and inspired to give their time and their talents to this great new art.

Recognition of the motion picture as an art by the great universities marks the beginning of a new day in motion picture work. It paves the ways for the motion picture's Shakespeares.

I wish it were possible here to draw aside the curtains of the future and to peer at what is to come, for the future, I have no fear, will be great.

William Kennedy Laurie Dickson, Edison's early laboratory assistant, far back in 1896 forecast the future of the motion picture.

"It is the crown and flower of the nineteenth century magic," he said, "the crystallization of eons of groping enchantments. In its wholesome, sunny, and accessible laws are possibilities undreamt of by the occult love of the East: the conservative wisdom of Egypt, the jealous erudition of Babylon, the guarded mysteries of Delphic and Eleusinian shrines. It is the earnest of the coming age, when the great potentialities of life shall no longer be in the keeping of cloister and college, of money bag, but shall overflow to the nethermost portions of the earth at the command of the humblest heir of the divine intelligence."

I agree with Terry Ramsaye when he says, "Will Hays himself could say no more, to-day."

The Coming
of
Sound

CHAPTER IV

The rapid and amazing adaptation of sound to motion
picture entertainment since the fall of 1926 has led to the
entirely erroneous belief that talking pictures are something
new under the sun, when, as a matter of fact, the development of sound was certainly corallary with, and some say,
was even the forerunner of the moving picture.

We know that Thomas A. Edison was looking for eyes
for his phonograph when he produced what turned out to
be the first marketable motion picture machine. And there
is much evidence to prove that scientists here and abroad
were engaged more than fifty years ago in making photographs of sound. There was, for instance, a Doctor Czer-
mak, of Vienna, who, in 1862 succeeded in photographing
the vocal chords in action although he did not, it is true,
attempt to record the sound vibrations; and there was a
Professor Eli Whitney Blake, of Brown University, who sixteen years later is reputed to have made pictures of the vibrations of a microphone diaphragm by means of a mirror
which cast a light on a photographic plate.

Instances of other experiments, similar to the many which
resulted in the invention of a commercially possible moving
picture, were from time to time recorded, leading up to the
time of Professor Demeny's "Chronophotophone" in 1892,

about which very little is known, and to the time of Edison's "Kinetoscope" in 1894 which, however crudely it was done, certainly synchronized sound with pictures. Like the peep-show pictures, the Kinetoscope was a one-man device, ear tubes being used to catch the sound. Public demonstrations were held at Raff and Gammon's amusement parlors at 1199 Broadway but the demand for the first "talkie" was so slight that the device was soon withdrawn.

In the years that immediately followed the withdrawal of the Kinetoscope, scientists continued their investigations. They worked quietly, as is the way of science, out of the public's eye, being, for the most part, content to wait until they had learned the essential facts about recording sound before making known their discoveries. When they did speak they were able to speak of a commercially successful article; they were ready to turn out an almost finished product. That is why sound has come into universal use with such amazing rapidity. It was delivered on a silver platter in 1926 and the industry had only to adapt itself to its use. To me the most interesting phase in the whole development has been the ease with which the producing companies and the theatres have adjusted themselves to so revolutionary an addition.

It is, of course, not within the scope of an article of this nature to go into the claims of various inventors as to their share in the development of talking pictures. Much has been said recently about men like Eugene Augustin Lauste, formerly an employe of Mr. Edison, and about his early experiments with talking pictures. Unquestionably the work of many men has gone into the perfection of the present talking devices. Almost every great invention is the result of the combined efforts of scientists. There can be in these pages, therefore, no attempt to place final responsibility. Such a matter is for the inventors, the patents office, and the users of sound to decide. It is sufficient to say that there is evidence that Lauste, about 1907, was demonstrating a sound and film device in London. He did not meet with great success apparently and was never able to market his product for any widespread use. In an interview printed in The New York World, Mr. Lauste attributed his failure to the breaking up of his company during the war. Most of his stockholders were Germans, and the necessary capital for future developments was not forthcoming.

Carl Laemmle, president of Universal Pictures Corporation, tells an interesting story of his early experiments with sound. Twenty years ago he imported from Germany a device which he advertised as the "greatest improvement in the moving picture." The name of the instrument was Synchroscope and the first exhibition was in Chicago for the benefit of exhibitors and representatives of the press. Confidentially Mr. Laemmle explained that "the craze for talking pictures will be even greater than the present craze for ordinary moving pictures."

There were others who rather more than half-believed the Universal Company's president. *Billboard,* for instance, in an editorial at the time asked: "Is the moving picture business about to be revolutionized? Has the time arrived when vaudeville houses can put on a whole bill by machinery? ... "I was fairly stunned the other day," said the *Billboard* writer, "when I witnessed a performance that was so startlingly realistic that I don't hesitate to say the questions already are answered in the affirmative."

For a time the Synchroscope was highly successful. Many exhibitors put in their orders and deliveries were accelerated. Other exhibitors who did not order the talking device made up for the deficit by engaging singers, and the day of the song-slides came into popularity. Still others attempted to make their own sound accompaniment through off-stage noises.

Upper—A scene from Cecil B. DeMille's "The King of Kings,"
a Pathe picture.
Lower—On the Universal sound stage—showing the sound crane used
in producing "Broadway."

At last the Synchroscope failed and was withdrawn. The difficulty was that there were not enough sound-films to meet the market's demand. The supply was exhausted. Another reason for failure was that the phonograph records which were used were capable of holding material for only two reels while the theatres were demanding four and five reels.

About 1908, Edison again turned his attention to the talking picture, this time with a device known as the Cameraphone which coupled a phonograph with a film projector by means of a wire belt. Making a Cameraphone picture was very simple. A phonograph record was selected and then the recording artist was photographed until the synchronization was at least passable. Of course the synchronization was not perfect. Today it would be instantly rejected but in those days close-ups had not come into popular use. Nobody had thought of throwing the head and face on a full screen and lip-movement was not regarded as important. Proponents of the Cameraphone argued with some justification that perfect synchronization was not imperative.

For a short time the Cameraphone flourished. It was admittedly a novelty, however, and while the world is always interested in novelties, it soon tires of them. The Cameraphone ceased to be popular, and since improvements were not forthcoming, the device vanished from the market until 1913 when Mr. Edison again launched a talking device.

An interesting story is told of the premiere of the Cameraphone, or the Kinetophone as it had come to be known. It was on a Monday afternoon, February 17, 1913, that three men set out to judge the audience reaction to Edison's newest invention. Those men were: Mr. Edison, John J. Murdock, and Martin Beck. Four theatres had been chosen for the experiments—the Colonial, the Fifth Avenue, Union

Square and the Alhambra. On the program of each of those theatres was the announcement: "Thomas A. Edison presents his latest and greatest invention, talking motion pictures, or the Kinetophone."

The *New York Times* reviewed the events which led up to that afternoon's experiment. Mr. Edison had perfected his invention on his shops at Orange, N. J., and had tried out the results on a small theatre adjoining his studio. A scene from Shakespeare's Julius Caesar was photographed with sound. Then there was a short lecture explaining the device, concluding with the breaking of a china dish. A violinist, a singer, and a pianist were on the program, and the whole was concluded with the barking of a dog.

A review of the showing in the papers of the day reveals the following interesting comment: "For the present at least the prophecy that the 'talkies' soon will supplant grand opera or the legitimate drama seems to be fantastical. It was stated that soon well-known players of the legitimate stage will be seen and heard in the 'talkies.' Then no doubt the invention will give greater pleasure to critical audiences."

The reviewer's comment was, for the time being at any rate, accurate. The Cameraphone did not become a sensation. Exhibitors shied away from it and within a short time it was withdrawn from the market. Not until 1921 was there another definite attempt to reach the public with talking pictures.

In that year D. W. Griffith, always a pioneering spirit, showed his picture "Dream Street" at the Town Hall in New York City with a sound accompaniment. The device he used was known as the Photokinema and the dialogue consumed about 200 feet of film. It was an interesting experiment and many of the leading figures in the industry were in the Town Hall for the showing. Griffith was warmly applauded for his efforts but the general belief was that talking pictures were still far off in the future.

Another name appears in the early history of sound—the name of Dr. Lee DeForest. Dr. DeForest in 1907 is said to have perfected a vacuum amplifying tube. About 1923 reports became current about the Phonofilm. Since then law suits have developed relative to patent rights, and those suits are still pending. Whatever the outcome may be, the name of Dr. DeForest is an interesting and important one in connection with the history of talking pictures.

The Modern Talking Picture

Chapter V

So far we have traced, however sketchily, the history of sound. Now we come to the great new volume in the history of motion pictures which is the record of the commercial development of talking pictures as we know them today. Here we enter into an entirely new phase of the motion pictures. Henceforth let no one make the mistake of regarding sound simply as an embellishment. Sound today is far more important than an effect. The talking picture is, in itself, a distinctive art-form.

In order to understand fully how and why talking pictures developed as quickly as they did, it is necessary first to review the motion picture situation as it existed early in 1926, at a time when motion pictures had reached what appeared to be a peak in popularity. One hundred million of our people each week were patronizing the 20,000 motion picture theatres; the studios in Hollywood, in an effective endeavor to meet the demands of the market for 800 feature pictures a year, were operating at their maximum capacity. Competition had never been keener. Every company was vying with every other company to attract the ablest writers, and the most efficient technicians. Hundreds of thousands of dollars were being spent on new effects, while an insatiable public demanded always something new.

In the larger cities competition had become so keen that the theatres, forced to fill their seats, inaugurated a system

of stage presentations which for a time threatened to relegate
the picture to a position of secondary importanace. One
elaborate revue after another was cast as bait before the
public. Overhead costs mounted as a consequence, while the
margin of profit showed slight tendency to increase. A
physician looking at the industry would have been forced
to report that, while the patient was fundamentally sound
and healthy, he was suffering from local disorders of a decidedly uncomfortable nature.

It was into such a situation then, that sound was destined
to project itself. Sound came at the opportune moment. The
field was fallow. Early in 1926 engineers, who had been
quietly and persistently studying the application of sound
to moving pictures, began to hint that they had at last progressed far enough in their experiments to warrant the belief
that commercially successful talking pictures could be produced and marketed. The producers themselves were the first
to hear such reports: but the producers, with few exceptions,
received the sound proposals, if not with indifference, at least
with incredulity. They were not over-cautious, but in the
past they had been the victims of glittering reports of sound.
They chose wisely to wait for developments. The engineers,
however, were insistent.

For five years—that is, since 1921—they had been studying
the use of sound with pictures, hoping to devise ways and
means of applying what they had learned about the transmission of sound via the telephone, the radio, and the phonograph to the development of a special technique relating to
talking pictures. The problem was not primarily one of
synchronizing sound and moving pictures. That was a
mechanical problem which could readily be solved. Their
real problem was to produce *satisfactory qualities of sound
in adequate volume.* By applying the identical principles
which they had used in successfully transmitting the voice

over great distances on the telephone, the engineers succeeded in recording and amplifying sound in conjunction with motion pictures.

As so often happens, several groups of scientists, each working independently of the other, began their experiments at about the same time. One group consisted of the engineers of the Bell Telephone Laboratories; another group consisted of engineers of the General Electric Company. The findings of both groups reached the present perfection approximately at the same time, but since the devices emanating from the Bell Laboratories, jointly owned by the American Telephone and Telegraph Company and Western Electric, were given to the public first, it will serve our purpose here to consider that development initially.

The Bell Laboratories development was carried forward on two major lines: firstly, the recording of sound on disc records operating in synchronism with the film; and, secondly, the recording of sound on the edge of the film itself by means of a photo-electric cell.

As I have indicated, when the news of the new sound device reached the industry, there was a definite tendency to leave sound alone. To one man, however, sound with pictures made an instant appeal. That man was Sam Warner, one of the four Warner brothers who had been producing pictures for a number of years. Sam Warner liked mechanical devices. He was an early radio enthusiast, and it was not difficult to induce him to visit the Bell Laboratories for a sight of the new talking device. Mr. Warner saw and appreciated the talking device. He wanted it. He wanted it badly, and immediately he planned to interest in the device his three brothers—Harry Warner, Major Albert Warner, and Jack Warner. Harry Warner, president of the company, shook his head. He knew pathetic stories about men who had dabbled in sound. But by persistence Sam Warner succeeded at last in getting his brother's consent to attend a demonstration.

That demonstration was destined to make a revolutionary change in the motion picture industry for Harry Warner, like his brother Sam, saw and was convinced. He was ready to throw the entire resources of his company behind the untried talking device, to stake everything, including his future, on one high throw. The great success which has come to his company is attributable to the courage which Harry Warner displayed on that occasion.

The immediate result of the two demonstrations—one for Sam Warner and one for Harry Warner—was that, in April, 1926, the Western Electric Company licensed Warner Brothers to produce talking pictures under its system and patents. The Warners elected to use the disc-method and the name they chose for their device was the Vitaphone. The first experiments were made in the old Vitagraph Studio in Flatbush, Brooklyn.

At that time Warner Brothers were completing the new John Barrymore picture called *Don Juan*. The production represented a large investment. Convinced that the success of the Vitaphone depended largely on its proper introduction to the public, the Warners decided to make the Barrymore film their first Vitaphone picture, and to show it at the only theatre in the world equipped for the Vitaphone—their own theatre at Broadway and 52nd Street, New York City. The New York Philharmonic Orchestra, under the direction of Henry Hadley, was engaged to make the synchronized musical accompaniment of the picture.

It was about this time that Harry Warner telephoned me to tell me of his plans. He had decided to offer half a dozen Vitaphone short subjects as a prelude to the feature picture and he wanted me to speak from the screen on behalf of the industry. I consented, of course, and a few days later

I accompanied Mr. Warner and other officials of his company to the Manhattan Opera House where I stood in front of a microphone and camera and said my piece—with gestures.

Because it was the first speech ever recorded for talking pictures, I shall herewith repeat the words I spoke that day:

"No story ever written for the screen is as dramatic as the story of the screen itself.

"Tonight marks another step in that story.

"Far indeed have we advanced from that few seconds of the shadow of a serpentine dancer thirty years ago when the motion picture was born—to this, the first public demonstration of the Vitaphone which synchronizes the reproduction of sound with the reproduction of action.

"And farther and farther ahead is the future of pictures, as far-flung as all the tomorrows, rendering greater and still greater service as the chief amusement of the majority of all our people and the sole amusement of millions and millions, exercising an immeasurable influence as a living, breathing thing on the ideas and ideals, the customs and costumes, the hopes and the ambitions of countless men, women and children.

"In the presentation of these pictures, music plays an invaluable part. Too, the motion picture is a most potent factor in the development of a national appreciation of good music. Now that service will be extended as the Vitaphone shall carry symphony orchestrations to the town halls of the hamlets.

"It has been said that the art of the musician is ephemeral, that he creates but for the moment. Now, neither the artist nor his art will ever die.

"Long experimentation and research by the Western Electric and the Bell Laboratories, supplemented by the efforts of Warner Brothers, have made this great new instrument possible, and to them and to all who have contributed to this achievement I offer my congratulations and best wishes.

"To the Warner Brothers, to whom is due credit for this great premiere, marking the beginning of a new era in music and motion pictures, I offer my felicitations and sincerest appreciation.

"It is an occasion with which the public and the motion picture industry are equally gratified.

"It is another great service—and 'Service is the supreme commitment of life.' "

A few sultry summer weeks then passed and in the meanwhile New York City was being made acquainted with the new and mysterious name, Vitaphone. The newspapers carried display advertisements; billboards were inundated with the title. A skeptical industry looked on with interest, and with doubt. Then on the evening of August 6, 1926, the Vitaphone had its premiere.

There were many distinguished persons in the audience at the Warner Theatre that night. It was more than a usual first-night gathering. It was an occasion. Promptly at the appointed hour the curtains parted and I saw myself on the screen. I heard my own voice speaking the same words I had spoken in the studio weeks before. In the darkness I said to myself, "A new miracle has been wrought and I have had a part in it."

In addition to the feature picture and my introductory speech Martinelli and Marion Talley sang. Mischa Elman and Zimbalist played their violins. Anna Case, assisted by a famous dancing team and by the Metropolitan Opera chorus, offered a Spanish song. The entire first half of the program was sensational; the second half was more than sensational. It was reassuring. The next day the newspapers commented favorably, some of them enthusiastically. The industry was interested but it was not completely convinced. Synchronized music—yes; singing—maybe; talking pictures—well, that was not likely. It was an interesting experiment, a more than ordinarily fine novelty, a great improvement over anything attempted in sound before; but for general use— well, very few people could believe it. The theatres were not equipped. It would cost money—too much money; it would revolutionize the business. The gamble was too great.

The four Warner brothers, however, were certain in their own minds that pictures with sound had come to stay. They had a faith that would not be shaken. They proceeded to synchronize other pictures with music, to make short subjects with operatic and Broadway stars. They proposed to equip other theatres as fast as they could.

By heroic efforts one hundred theatres were equipped for talking pictures within six months. Then the Warners learned with a shock that the cost of equipment was much greater than they had anticipated. They found it necessary to form a financing corporation which would buy the equipment from Western Electric and sell it on deferred payments to the theatres. Their investment in sound increased. They were in it to the limit of their resources.

Several months hobbled by and then the Warners made another epochal picture. It was called *The Jazz Singer* and Al Jolson was the star. In it Jolson, one of the most popular musical comedy stars of the times not only sang but actually *spoke* from the screen. The opening was set for the evening of October 6, 1927—a little more than a year after the first Vitaphone picture had been shown. All plans were completed. Then occurred one of those inexplicable tragedies with which life is filled.

During the last week in September Sam Warner complained of not feeling well. He had a bad cold. It was not of any great consequence, he thought, but when the time

The late Sam Warner whose early interest in talking pictures led to the development of Vitaphone by Warner Brothers' Pictures, Inc.

came for him and his brothers, Jack and Albert, to leave for New York for the premiere of *The Jazz Singer*, he decided not to go. Jack went alone. Albert stayed with Sam. Two days later Sam Warner went to the hospital. A sinus was infected. Quickly the poison flowed through his body. A surgeon operated. Jack Warner turned around and started home immediately. Harry Warner forgot the premiere and caught a train for Hollywood. Across the continent the two brothers raced with death. At first the news which met them at every station was reassuring. Then there was a relapse. Harry Warner, two days behind Jack, left the train and engaged an aeroplane. He reached Los Angeles on the morning of October 5. His brother had been dead for three hours.

Fiction writers and playwrights have always been fond of the theme which says that "the show must go on" though the players are sick at heart. By an odd coincidence Jolson's picture, *The Jazz Singer,* was based on that very theme. It was the theme of another Warner picture, *The Singing Fool,* The show had to go on. Plans for the premiere were continued. On the success of the Jolson picture rested largely the future of sound. Yet the man who had first seized upon the idea of sound pictures lay dead, and his three brothers who had backed his faith, were in Hollywood with his body. But the show went on. The premiere was a startling success. Within a few weeks the picture was to be a sensation. It attracted more people to the theatre than almost any other picture ever produced.

The Jazz Singer marked the beginning of a great rush to sound. The industry which had been waiting for assurance of the practicability of sound was at length convinced. The turning point had been reached. Today we reckon the evening of October 6, 1927, as the beginning of a new phase in motion pictures. From that evening on sound became the imperative element in production.

In the meanwhile, William Fox, president of the Fox Film Corporation, had been working with Theodore W. Case, of the Case Laboratories, and with Earl I. Sponable, another young inventor, in the development of a talking system which used the sound-on-film method. For fifteen years, ever since he was a student at Yale University, Theodore Case had been experimenting with sound-on-film. In 1916, then a chemical student at Cornell, Earl Sponable joined forces with Case. Their problem was to find substances which were extremely sensitive to light.

The war came on and the young experimenters put aside their work, devoting their entire time to development of infra-red light rays which could be used in signalling ships. As a result of their efforts, many convoys en route to France, were kept in line. After the cessation of fighting, the young inventors returned to Auburn, N. Y., and resumed their experiments with sound-on-film. 1922 they had perfected a light bulb called an AEO light which was so sensitive to sound vibrations that lines of sound could be photographed on the film.

It was not until the Spring of 1926, however, that Mr. Case and Mr. Sponable presented their discoveries to William Fox. They had waited until they were sure of themselves and of the practicability of their idea. Mr. Fox immediately saw the great possibilities of sound. He agreed to finance further experiments. No time was lost. In June, 1926, experiments were continued under Mr. Fox's sponsorship and two months later the Fox Case Corporation had been organized. Courtland Smith, who had been with me in the Post Office Department and who was secretary of Motion Picture Producers and Distributors of America, was made head of the new organization. A new plant was opened at Tenth Avenue and 54th Street and the name chosen for the new device was *Movietone*.

The Fox-Case Company at first turned its attention to development of talking newsreels, in which it was proposed to record sound as well as the action of current news events. Its second consideration was the production of Movietone short subjects.

The first public showing of Fox Movietone subjects was set for the evening of January 21, 1927, in connection with the premiere of the Fox feature film, "What Price Glory?" That was at the Sam H. Harris Theatre and the Movietone consisted of songs by Raquel Meller, the Spanish singer who had made an astounding success in this country a few months before and who was already a great star throughout Europe. Not until May 25 was an all-Movietone program ready for public exhibition. On that night the Fox Company presented "Seventh Heaven," a silent-film synchronized with music. The preliminary program consisted of Movietone shorts. Raquel Meller again was shown and Charles (Chic) Sales was seen and heard in a short comedy sketch called "They're Coming After Me." Ben Bernie's orchestra played, Gertrude Lawrence sang a song she had introduced with great success in the first Charlot's Revue. The preliminary program was concluded with a newsreel which was designed to be historic in the industry. That was the take-off of Colonel Charles A. Lindbergh on his New York to Paris flight.

Audiences in New York heard the whir and roar of the aeroplane's motor, listened to the shouts of farewell, to the gasps of the onlookers as plane hesitated, skipped, and then leaped from the ground into the air. It is history now how the world went mad about Lindbergh. Millions of people wanted to see him. They wanted to hear as well as to see his take-off. The Movietone record was a sensation.

By September, 1927, the first Fox feature picture had been synchronized before its Broadway showing. That picture was "Sunrise," and by the week of October 28, the first all-Movietone newsreel was shown at the Roxy Theatre. Six weeks later the Movietone News was a weekly feature. Exhibitors sought the newsreels as quickly as their houses were wired.

New developments came swiftly in the first months of 1928. Courtland Smith's organizing ability was being felt everywhere. His was a tremendous job of pioneering but with the ardent support of Mr. Fox and other colleagues he strode rapidly ahead. Experiments had already proved that the complete sound equipment could be transported in one and one-half ton trucks and a whole fleet of such trucks was ordered. The first all-talking comedy, known as "The Family Picnic," was presented to the public.

Since it was already obvious that sound pictures would sweep the country, Fox-Case decided to issue two instead of one Movietone News each week. A few months later the number was increased to three a week and only a short while before this writing it was found necessary to issue four newsreels a week.

Mr. Fox has frequently said that he was led to take part in the development of talking pictures not simply because he saw commercial possibilities in them but because he believed they would be a benefit to mankind. Especially is he interested in the educational possibilities of the talking screen, and it is not surprising that he developed the invaluable plan of bringing the great personalities of the world before the camera. The first crowned monarch ever thus to appear on the screen was King Alfonso XIII of Spain. Others followed rapidly. King George V of England, the Prince of Wales, Premier Benito Mussolini, Marshal Foch, President von Hindenburg, President Hainish of Austria, Raymond Poincare, the Crown Prince of Sweden, David Lloyd George, and Ramsay MacDonald are to be found

among the notable governmental officials who have spoken
from the screen. Then there have been others like George
Bernard Shaw, the great dramatist, who has refused persistently to visit America, Dr. Hugo Eckener, Sir Arthur
Conan Doyle. All of these men have had messages for
America and for the world. They have been brought into
close touch with our people. A spirit of friendship has been
created.

At the same time many of America's leaders have
spoken from the screen, among them President Hoover,
former President Coolidge, General John J. Pershing, Chief
Justice William Howard Taft, former Governor Alfred E.
Smith, Colonel Lindbergh, and Thomas A. Edison. This
entire purpose of William Fox in bringing the world's personalities to the world's peoples has been a very real contribution to the world's welfare.

The Recording
of Sound
Pictures

Chapter VI

We must again retrace our steps to that time when the Bell Laboratories authorized their scientists to study the application of sound to motion pictures. We find another group of engineers, with the same end in view, at work under the direction of General Electric Company.

The first product of the General Electric Company laboratories was known as the Pallophotophone. It was the conception of Dr. C. A. Hoxie and the development of the trained experts in the General Electric's laboratories in Schenectady. The Pallophotophone is a sound-on-film device and one of its distinguishing characteristics is the powerful auditorium public speakers or amplifiers of the cone type which were invented by Dr. C. W. Hewlett.

For about six years study was devoted to the Pallophotophone before the public was allowed to see and hear the results. In the early part of 1927 a series of short subjects was produced and exhibited in a Schenectady theatre. So marked was their success that Radio Corporation of America became interested in the device. The name of the instrument was changed to the Photophone and a corporation known as RCA Photophone was organized, with headquarters at 411 Fifth Avenue. There a series of exhibitions was arranged and many of the important executives of the industry as well as many exhibitors came in 1928 to see and hear the Photophone.

Toward the end of 1927, Paramount Famous Lasky completed a great epic-picture of the air called "Wings." It gave a wide public demonstration to the RCA-General Electric device. Studios meanwhile had been opened and other pictures were synchronized. The development of equipment was continued in the laboratories and manufacturing plants of the Radio Corporation of America, the General Electric Company, and the Westinghouse Electric and Manufacturing Company.

The success of *The Jazz Singer* was the signal for all the producing companies to enter the sound field. Additional licenses were granted by Electrical Research Products, Inc., on behalf of the Western Electric Company, to Paramount Famous Lasky; Metro-Goldwyn-Mayer; United Artists; First National Pictures; Universal Pictures; Metropolitan Sound Studios; Hal Roach Studios; the Victor Talking Machine Company; and more recently to Columbia Pictures and to Sono-Art Productions. Among the companies licensed under the RCA Photophone system of recording are Pathé Exchange, Radio Pictures, Educational Film Exchanges, Pathé Sound News, Tiffany-Stahl, Mack Sennett and others. By the fall of 1929 more than five thousand theatres in this country possessed sound equipment.

Almost over-night sound had ceased to be merely a novelty. It was no longer a development for the future. It was with us alive, present. "When, how, and for how much can I get equipment?" the theatre owners began wiring to ask. "How soon can sound stages and producing equipment be in place?" the production heads wanted to know. Sound, sound, sound! That was the whole cry. What followed is now history. Skepticism died in the thundering approval of the public. Those who waited would be likely to watch the procession pass by. The bandwagon had come along and as many as possible were climbing aboard. Although less than two years have passed as this is written, sound has become a major part of motion pictures. The balance has turned in favor of dialogue. Several thousand theatres have been equipped for reproducing sound. Every studio has its sound devices for recording. A new technique in writing and acting has developed. Changes have come with lightning-like rapidity. Sound is in, and on, the air.

Solution of the two major problems of synchronization of sound made possible the success of talking pictures.

The first problem was to record sounds completely and accurately, and then to reproduce those sounds just as completely and just as accurately. The discovery of the relationship between sound impedances and electric impedances offered the solution to the first problem. The radio and the orthophonic Victrola had already made possible the complete and accurate recording and transmission of voices with the picture.

The second problem was to reproduce the recorded sounds with such volume as to make them heard in all parts of a theatre auditorium. Vacuum tubes pick up the sound and amplify it and loud speakers take it to every section of the theatre. The addition of pictures, in synchronization, perfected the talking picture.

Transmission of sound was first solved for improved long-distance telephone service. Vacuum tube amplifiers were evolved for the purpose of stepping-up the voice or its electrical impulse at regular intervals. Then came the loudspeaker, which throws the voice hundreds of feet from the transmitter. With the transmission accounted for, the only remaining step was the complete and accurate recording of sound. Studies along such lines quickly provided the solution to the problem. It was found that in making phonograph records directly from the performer through a megaphone to a diaphragm stylus and wax disc, all the sound frequencies were not included. What was needed was a more sensitive

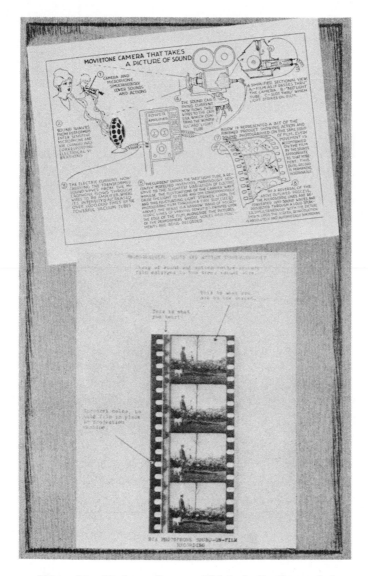

Upper—How Movietone Operates. This is the Fox-Case method.
Lower—The film as used in RCA Photophone productions.

system; and that was what the experimenters found. Their plan was to have the performer sing or speak into a microphone as in radio and to have the electric energy, motivated by the sound waves, move the stylus against the wax disc. Thus was accurate recording made possible.

There are two distinctive methods of recording sound. One is the disc method, the other is the sound-on-film. The first is not unlike recording for phonographs. In the latter case, the sound record is photographed on the film itself. Theatre equipment is available which can be used with either of the methods or with both. The only difference lies in the "pick-up" apparatus used at the projector. The amplifiers and horns are identical, and productions of both sorts can be used on the same program, a simple switching operation permitting immediate change from one method to the other.

Both recordings are electrically done. The voice or music is picked up by a microphone which generates a small electric current whose variations correspond to the sound waves. In disc recording, this current controls an electric-magnetic recording-stylus whose movements cut the record on a wax disc in the usual manner, with undulations of the groove corresponding to the sound waves. In sound-on-film recording, the amount of light falling on the moving film is made to vary in accordance with the fluctuations of the microphone current and so a photographic record corresponding to these fluctuations—and, therefore, to the voice or music— becomes impressed on the film. The disc records are similar to the best types of phonograph records except that they are much larger and run at about half standard speed. This enables each record to play throughout a whole reel. The film used is the same as the ordinary film except that one frame at the beginning is marked in order to denote the starting point.

With the film method, the sound record consists of a band about one-eighth of an inch wide called the "sound track" running down one side of the film. It is made of microscopic lines and in the case of the Movietone, the spacing of these lines depends on the pitch of sound which was recorded at that moment. The difference of intensity of the lines depends on the loudness of the sound—that is, the greater the contrast between the light and dark lines, the louder the sound. An ordinary beam of light from a high intensity lamp is focused on the sound track through a system of lenses and an aperture plate. The light which passes through the moving film will vary in intensity according to the variations of the lines recording in the sound track. This light falls on a photo-electric cell which produces a small electric current whose variations correspond to the light and, therefore, to the sound which was recorded. The Photophone arrangement differs in that the lines are long and short, rather than light and dense. They resemble nothing so much as a hair comb with some of the teeth broken. In the industry it is spoken of as a hill and dale arrangement.

The current from the amplifiers is converted into sound by means of sound projectors consisting of receivers and horns located at the screen. The number of horns and their size depends upon the size and acoustic properties of the theatre. The horns are placed directly behind the screen so that a perfect illusion that the voice and the music are coming from the screen may be obtained in all parts of the theatre.

The Future Industry

Chapter VII

The immediate effect of sound has been to increase attendance at motion picture theatres by millions. Vast new audiences have been reached and these will be held as the development continues and as talking pictures become better and better. With the same familiarity with which the public receive motion pictures under its own affectionate name of "movies," the public has accepted talking pictures under the name of "talkies."

At first there was a wide variance of opinion as to the future of sound. Many men in the industry believed that sound would not last. It took public response to convince many of them that sound was here to stay. It is but fair to say of them that when they were convinced, they did not hesitate to reverse their opinions.

Sound, of course, has wrought great changes in the technique of motion picture production. Nowhere has this change been so noticeable as in the methods of direction and of scenario writing. Incidentally, of course, great new fields of dramatic material were opened up for the screen. Plays and stories which had depended largely on dialogue or on their psychological development for success became usable for the first time. The writing of natural speech became imperative. To the everlasting credit of the screen writers, let it be said that they are speedily mastering the new technique. The pictures today offer an outstanding example of the effective use of simple and telling dialogue.

An early fear that sound would end the careers of many
well-known actors who had been developed for the screen
without previous stage experience has been to a large extent
dissipated by time. The public still seems to prefer its screen
stars, with the result that not many screen players have
been discarded. They have simply had their ranks added
to by attractive personalities imported from the speaking
stage. If an actor cannot speak lines with ordinary ability
or suffers from vocal impediments, of course he loses his
value. Several foreign stars, who could not speak English
and who declined to devote sufficient time to mastery of the
language, were unneeded when talking became a necessary
addition to the film.

The public has always been drawn to motion pictures by
the personalities of the players as much as by the stories
and I do not believe that the public will ever materially
change its habits. And isn't it true, as a matter of fact, that
even the stage depends very little upon voices? Very few
producers demand perfect diction. The stage and the screen
depend largely on types, and this is especially true of motion
pictures because the screen is now and always has been the
exponent of realism. It places characters in human situations
and moves them through scenes peopled by ordinary figures
of the world. Without meaning any disparagement of the
stage, I still say that it does not approach the motion pictures
in naturalness.

Many stage voices are unnatural when transferred to a
record. Actors have the habit of declaiming their .lines.
They speak to the tenth row, or to the gallery. In front of
the microphone, the slightest whisper is audible. One's
natural conversational voice is preferable. And motion picture actors have the ability to hold their own in natural
speech.

Of course, many important actors and actresses who have

achieved distinction on the legitimate stage have met with success in talking pictures. They will continue to find success and the industry will always welcome trained talent, for its purpose is to produce pictures which are entertaining and dramatic and artistic, and those who are best qualified to appear in such pictures will always be selected.

In the last few months much has been learned about the possibilities of sound. Every new picture has marked an advance. Directors are learning how to save all the advantages of the silent picture while they are adding the qualities of sound. Their progress has been little short of dazzling. They have been forced to deal with a new instrument. They have had to master a new technique.

At first we thought it necessary to have absolutely sound-proof studios. Today we make sound pictures outdoors. We have made mistakes but we are getting rapidly away from the early errors. Every new picture marks a really great advance.

Today sound is new. Tomorrow there will be something else—the enlarged screen, the third dimension.

I do not think I am too visionary when I predict for tomorrow a motion picture flashed on the screen as large as the ordinary stage, the figures moving in perspective, speaking naturally, all in the vivid colors of life. That day, in fact, is just around the corner.

NUMBER THIRTY-EIGHT
UNIVERSITY OF WASHINGTON CHAPBOOKS
Edited by Glenn Hughes

THE AMERICAN INFLUENCE IN FRANCE

The American Influence In France

By

Philippe Soupault

1930
UNIVERSITY OF WASHINGTON BOOK STORE
Seattle

THE AMERICAN INFLUENCE
IN FRANCE

This essay was written expressly for the Chap-books. It was translated from the French by Babette and Glenn Hughes.

THE AMERICAN INFLUENCE
IN FRANCE

ITH very few exceptions the writers of
the pre-war generation had but one
aim: to analyze life, and therefore to
draw deliberately away from it. By
contrast, those who in the first flush
of their youth were witnesses of death and destruc-
tion, those who have survived the cataclysm of
stupidity (which it seemed to them could never be
ended), have turned with a kind of fever towards
life. In doing so they have broken away from the
prejudices commonly called traditions.

Naturally enough, they have been disowned,
scoffed at, and persecuted by those who made up
the earlier generation, those friends of tradition,
who, it must be remembered, are responsible for
the war.

Nothing could better illustrate these points of
view than the prevailing attitudes toward the
United States. To members of the older generation the United States is simply a foreign nation,

a friendly nation, an allied nation, an enemy nation, a creditor nation, or what not.   To their
minds there is scarcely any distinction between
Essen (Germany) and Pittsburgh.   Two nations
. . . . . somewhere outside of France.   The older
generation will never be corrected in their thinking.   They are used to considering the world as a
lists where war must break out one day or another.
For these old Frenchmen the United States is
symbolized by its armed strength and by the dollar.
Thus much for their logic.   But they have also
created legends, and in this world of ready-made
images the United States still remains the country
of Fenimore Cooper's redskins, of Buffalo Bill's
cowboys, of millionaire uncles.* New York means
skyscrapers; Chicago, factories and meat-packers.
. . . . . And it must not be believed that a minority
thinks of the United States in these terms; after
careful thought one is forced to the conclusion that
an immense majority of Frenchmen still cling to
these childish illusions.

It is also true that for the so-called younger
writers, the actual discovery of America dates back

---

* One is reminded of this by the naïve book of Monsieur Abel Her-
mant (of the French Academy, of course), entitled *Les Transatlantiques*.

only a few years.   But in spite of this fact, the influence of the United States has been enormous. Some writers submit unwillingly to it, some even revolt against it; others accept it willingly and even seek it.   And it was only ten years ago that the American influence could be summed up in the names of two poets: E. A. Poe and Walt Whitman. Ever since the efforts of Baudelaire to make known the work of Poe, the influence of the author of *Eureka* has steadily increased.   He has really become one of the masters of French literature, and his power over the French mind is enormous.*   Whitman, too, has played an important rôle.   He has, so to speak, given new life to French lyricism, which, until his time, was stifled in the prison of rules and cramped in the pillory of versification.   What he actually did was to strengthen and confirm a point of view expressed earlier by Arthur Rimbaud and other French poets.   Whitman completed their work.

In the eyes of literary Frenchmen of the pre-war generation, who treated literature as a religion and lived solely for it, the United States meant

---

* I shall cite here only three names, which form a chain: Baudelaire, Mallarmé, Paul Valéry.

simply two names: Poe and Whitman.   Present-
day writers have not the same respect for literature, nor the same devotion to it, yet they have
retained for Poe and Whitman an exceptional
tenderness.

Literature alone does not suffice the new generation.   Furthermore, the world created by these
two poets was not specifically American.   In spite
of them the United States remained an almost un-
assailable mystery.   The continent was veiled by
the haze of poetry.   The real voice of America
made itself heard finally in a much less literary
but a more definite—and more sentimental—way.
Before giving an historical account of this revelation, however, it seems to me advisable to make
very clear the essential difference between the two
opposing generations.

At the beginning of this essay, as an example
of one attitude toward the United States, I pointed
out that the writers, the thinkers, of the older generation, refused to consider nations as other than
abstractions.   This attitude of theirs is explained
by their lack of a taste for life.   They wished only
to think.   Those who came after them (and I refer
particularly to those who wrote in the shadow of

the war) escaped from abstract concepts and recovered the liveliest and wildest desire for life.

I recall that in 1918 my friends and I were always saying of men and things: "So and so is alive; such and such a thing is dead." Our manner of expression summed up our state of mind. We wanted to love life (with which we were disgusted) and we did love it. We had this desire not because we were young but because it had become a passion with us.

That was in 1918, 1919, 1920. . . . . Now let us go back a little.

At the very moment when French eyes were weary of seeing over and over again in the theatre those eternal and identical "slices of life," and when only the music-hall could touch us even a little, the cinema was born.

But our hopes for the cinema were exaggerated. The films proved to be lamentable, insignificant, boring. They were not stupid enough to be amusing, but the scenario writers put forth all their efforts to please the great public—that public which delights in melodrama and sentimental comedy— and the clever directors, wishing to bring forth our tears, sowed the film with tiny blue flowers.

The result was not always what had been intended. The spectators wept at first, then laughed. They saw a little girl stolen by evil tramps and then recovered accidentally by her parents; a poor mother and her dozen children beaten by a brutal and drunken husband, and finally avenged by alcohol and delirium tremens.*

The boredom of evenings that drew out like cigarette smoke, and that pulled our arms into a sleepy figure of the cross, flowered in the intense lives of the young men, my friends. We walked the cold and deserted streets seeking an accidental, a sudden, meeting with life. To distract ourselves we found it necessary to yoke the imagination with sensational dreams. For a time we found distraction in lurid periodicals—those papers which are more highly-colored than picture postcards. We scoured the world for them, and by means of them we participated in marvelous and bloody dramas which illuminated for an instant various parts of the earth. We were thirsty, terribly thirsty, for life at its strangest and strongest, and this life we drank like milk. One of us, the strongest of all,

---

* Certain very "modern" cinemas have conceived the idea of exhibiting these old films, but few spectators can laugh at them any more.

Jacques Vaché, declared: "I wish I were a trap-
per, or a bandit, a prospector, a hunter, a miner, or
a sheep-shearer."*

Then, one day we saw hanging on the walls
great posters as long as serpents. At every street-
corner a man, his face covered with a red handker-
chief, leveled a revolver at the peaceful passersby.
We imagined that we heard galloping hoofs, the
roar of motors, explosions, and cries of death. We
rushed into the cinemas, and realized immediately
that everything had changed. On the screen appeared the smile of Pearl White—that almost
ferocious smile which announced the revolution,
the beginning of a new world. At last we knew
that the cinema was not merely a perfected mechanical toy, but a terrible and magnificent reflection of life.

The dark little halls in which we sat became
living theatres of our laughter, our fury, and our
deepest feelings of pride. Through our wide-
open eyes we read the crimes, the farewells, the
extraordinary events, and above all (or in spite

---

* The charming letters of Jacques Vaché were published in 1919
(Sans Pareil) and form the most striking document of the so-called
war generation.

of all) the poetry of our age. We did not understand what was going on. We were living swiftly, passionately. It was a very beautiful period. Many elements, no doubt, contributed to its beauty, but the cinema of the U. S. A. was one of the brightest ornaments.

And even then we did not know Charlie Chaplin.

There is a man who has received from heaven the finest gift possible in this world, who knows better than anyone else how to long for things, who loves and who observes, who forgets and who amuses, and who is the most misunderstood man of the century.

The ingratitude of laughter and joy is stupefying. How astonishing it is that no writer has devoted his life to following, step by step, the evolution of this phenomenal human being. Of course he is rolling in gold, but he is nevertheless at the mercy of death. Consider for a moment what would happen were he to die. The violet (or mauve) veils of oblivion would swiftly cover his tomb, and the highest mausoleum in the world would not preserve his memory. Chaplin, no doubt, would be the first to laugh at all this, for he cares little for fame; but the fact that he scorns it is the very reason why we must take it seriously.

It has not yet occurred to us to express surprise at the minor importance attached to him who in France is called Charlot, but soon we shall realize the magnitude of his rôle.   Charlie Chaplin "invented" the cinema for us.   It probably was easy for him to do, but that is because he is a poet. Surely it is unnecessary to emphasize this fact, or to point out that for a long time now everyone has recognized the distance which separates Charlot's films from practically all other films.   Poetry is the most violent of all known acids.   It eats its way into the richest and strongest materials; its presence demands an entirely new structure. Chaplin's films illustrate this principle, and we are under the impression that ever since *The Immigrant* the most famous and most intelligent producers have done nothing but mark time.   Not one of them has even recognized the sublime trick of Charlie Chaplin which we poets call poetry.

The sudden appearance of Chaplin gave rise to laughter of the highest significance.   One may even say that Chaplin's comedy created a scandal. And so as not to lose their habit, the Parisian journalists cried "decadence," without attempting to understand the extraordinary success of this extraordinary actor.

It seems that Charlie Chaplin, with one stroke of his cane—such a smiling magician, too—was able to endow the American cinema with a marvelous vitality, an incredible superiority. All the films issuing from the studios of Los Angeles possessed the power to please. There were long sequences of action—without a single dull passage—portraying sensational abductions; there were the pictures of Douglas Fairbanks, of Rio Jim, and of Tom Mix; there were complicated stories ending in the robbing of banks, in violent deaths, in discoveries of gold mines; there was the huge, silent office, and the head of a man armed with a cigar, who sits thinking, and his thought encompasses the United States, the continent of America, the whole world. Near his head a telephone rings dully and brings his thought to earth. The soundless ringing of a bell in the cinema—does it not symbolize the final tragic desuetude of the note of a horn in the depth of a forest, of our own romantic Alfred de Vigny? Doors open and close; bronzed men, strong men, terribly refined or ter-

ribly frivolous women come and go with happiness
or unhappiness in their hands.

The American cinema brought to light all the
beauty of our epoch, and all the mystery of modern mechanics. But it was all done so simply, so
naturally, so unaffectedly, that one scarcely noticed
it. It was, however, one of the greatest and most
important of artistic discoveries. It created at one
blow a new world. And this new beauty, discov-
ered so easily, so naturally, was accompanied by a
technical perfection unknown until the present day.
The American picture-producers understood the
drama that lay hidden in a lock, in a hand, in a
drop of water.

The influence of this new force soon made itself
felt. All French poetry, I believe, submitted profoundly to its imprint. And the theatre, more
slowly, to be sure, but little by little, was trans-
formed by the contact. One can even notice—with
somewhat of a shock—that since the first appearance of films "made in the U. S. A." there has
begun an evolution in painting—an art which is
always slightly in the rear of poetry. I am certain
that painting will feel the influence of the new
conditions imposed by the cinema.

I shall even go so far as to make this rather
startling declaration: the cinema has brought us a
new desire.   It opens a window on the world.*
And this world we shall slowly discover.   Slowly
because the shores are veiled in mist, as well as
in artificial smoke.   So many third-rate journalists,
and reporters who write to flatter a public which
they imagine to be more uncivilized than it actually
is, have provided the people with ready-made
images!   We all know the French story of an
Englishman who landed for the first time on
French soil at Calais, and who, perceiving a red-
haired woman, wrote in his notebook: "In France
all the women have red hair."   According to these
journalists all houses in the United States are skyscrapers, all Americans dream only of making
money, all the railway trains are uncomfortable,
etc. . . .

Then essayists of a different sort began publishing more serious works which endeavored, with

* The same phenomenon occurred ten years later.   When the first
films from Soviet Russia were shown on the screen, one could easily
perceive the curiosity regarding the new Russia which they awakened in
all intellectual circles.   The political revolution had aroused political
passions, but this interest was not due to the fact that the event was
Russian, but merely that it was an historical phenomenon.

varying degrees of success, to complete the study begun by Alexis de Tocqueville in *La Democratie en Amerique*. But most of these writings were political and economic. Only an occasional detail satisfied our curiosity. The cinema still remained our best source of knowledge. Then, little by little, this medium of expression became international—I mean that it lost its distinctively American qualities. At the same time, whipping our curiosity and furthering our taste for the United States, came American music. Too often were we tempted to designate this music as jazz, and to consider it only as dance music, worthy at most of being heard in restaurants and cabarets. At first we refused to listen to it seriously. But, as even its enemies admit, it conquered France and all of Europe. We hesitated to call it music or to classify it as an art—it was too near to life.

And precisely because of that quality it exercises an enormous influence. It has helped us finally to discover and to understand the United States. I know, of course, that it is said to be not American, but negro. This point of view I refuse to discuss, first because it is silly, and second because it seems to me radically false. What remains profoundly true is that this music worked its way in and struck violently those whom the cinema had already awakened to the American influence. Thanks to this music, the poets took a new step forward.

I do not wish to recount in detail, as I have done in the case of the cinema, the influence of music and its various consequences. Suffice it to say that one no longer discusses this subject. But there is one observation which I consider it necessary always to make: European music for several centuries has been divided into two branches, popular music (songs, marches, operettas), and highbrow music, that is to say, concert music. American music, on the other hand, is of a single sort. Neither popular nor purely artistic (hermetic, one might say), it belongs utterly to life. And one need not fear to emphasize always this characteristic in whatever comes from the United States. One of the most definite qualities of the American influence resides in the close relationship between art and life.*

That, I believe, is the essential point of this

---

* By way of contrast to this statement one might note that European art exists on a misunderstanding. It escapes from life in order to return to it by a detour. This is a symptom of age and a warning of decadence.

essay. All other observations which one might make concerning the American influence in Europe spring from this one statement.

* * * *

It is not my business here to judge whether this influence, which increases year by year, is good or bad. It is my business merely to state clearly and honestly what the influence is. A strong, irresistible current has been set flowing in the last ten years. Its volume will be swollen by all the novelties within the power of the United States to create. Within the last year, for example, the European theatre has succumbed to the influence of New York. So it will be with one thing after another. From today on, it seems to me, the resistance of Europe will diminish.

Among the poets, and after all it is they who prove the most faithful witnesses of events, there is a new and friendly curiosity regarding American poetry. The state of a poet's soul, or we might say the state of soul of poets, is but a more brilliant reflection, a more glowing image, of the life of all the people.

American poetry seems to me at the present moment to be exceptionally vital. Its voice is heard from across the Atlantic. Already it modifies French poetry, which is the most individual and the most strictly regulated of all poetries. In France we listen to the American chants. All things coming to us from America astonish us, but only by means of the poets' imagery do we really comprehend the grandeur, the majesty, of this new civilization.

Today, when everything restricts us, when life becomes increasingly narrowed, when we would be inclined to retreat within ourselves, the American poets present us with an example of complete liberation. They show us the ways we must take. They make us stop and think, and realize that we are no longer the center of the world. They have no illusions regarding our little Europe: they look upon her as one part of the world, and their view is a universal one.

Her poetry is probably the least known of the rich contributions made by the United States, but probably also it is the most precious and the most fertile.

*   *   *   *

My only aim in this brief essay has been to trace

certain signs which the wind of time might efface tomorrow. In 1930 we know that the United States is one of the great nations of white civilization, but we know more than this—we know that a new spirit has been born. Henceforth the situation will be clear. There is the spirit of old Europe, varied and scintillating, centering in Vienna, Paris, London, Rome, and Berlin; there is the spirit of Moscow; and finally, there is the spirit of New York. Three poles.

At the start of this century we await the transformation of the world—an overthrow as great as the fall of Athens or the fall of Rome.